The Evolution of Biomechanics

Bringing movement theory back to life.

By Stephen Braybrook, MSc

AKA – The Movement Man

DM Press

The Evolution of Biomechanics

Published by DM Press
Copyright © 2016 Stephen Braybrook
ISBN 978-0-9955033-0-4

To my children Dillan and Maya.
May you always follow your own path.

CONTENTS

Acknowledgements

So many great people have influenced me and helped me along my journey that has led me to writing this book, that it is impossible to name them all. As I thank the few, I extend my gratitude equally to everyone whose path I may have crossed on my movement journey. This book is a product of many people and without their help, challenges, questions, conversations and sharing it would have not have been possible.

I would like to thank all of my close family and friends who have supported me along the way – each of you knows you who you are. And it is with eternal love and gratitude that I would like to make special mention to my mum Patricia and my dad John for their unequivocal support and belief in me; my gorgeous children Dillan and Maya for their daily inspiration and finally my wife Rebecca for her love, support, readiness to challenge me and patient translating, proof reading and editing duties. Your love and support means the world to me.

Ultimately, this book is dedicated to you, the reader. For by picking up this book you have become my fellow companion in human movement, joining me on my journey, which I am hopeful that mover by mover, we will evolve into an exodus.

A note from the 'translator'

For anyone who knows Stephen personally, you will already know that he is an expert in his subject. However, being dyslexic has occasionally proven to be highly problematic in his professional life. He has been misinterpreted, misunderstood, assumed stupid, sacked for incompetence due to paperwork issues and even now he still gets the occasional rap via social media for not making sense due to his spelling, sentence structure, syntax and/or grammatical errors.

Living with dyslexia as an often hidden disability can be frustrating, difficult and disheartening. Stephen's dyslexia makes communication via the written word very difficult and forming coherent sentences and overall structure is almost impossible, with the sense of narrative often lost. Like his thinking, his idea of a finished paragraph is not linear! This has proven a huge challenge in actually getting his ideas written down in a logical and coherent format, resulting in a slow, stilted and drawn out process to get this book finished.

Faced with these challenges I have taken it upon myself to help Stephen spread his message, as I strongly believe it is a message worth sharing. Initially we weren't quite sure how to term my role in the production of this book and in the end we have opted for 'translator'. The way that Stephen and I have worked together, is by him writing his ideas down as he wants them to be heard and then me going through and 'translating' from dyslexic English into something that is (hopefully) a logical, more readable format. This 'translation' process has been a labour of love and I hope that in the re-moulding of Stephen's words, sentences and structure, his ideas still shine through as he intended. For anyone who gets the chance, I cannot recommend highly enough that you experience Stephen's work verbally, from the man himself. Oration is his strongest medium of communication, where he is not bound by the restrictions of his dyslexia. He will intend to follow the release of this book with webinars and online lectures where people can experience his work orally as well as providing an opportunity for people to ask questions and engage with his work. In the meantime, I hope you enjoy this joint effort from the dyslexic, mad movement scientist and his sentence-structure loving wife!

-Rebecca Braybrook

About the author

 My love and fascination of human movement began at an early age. At seventeen years old I had a promising career in professional football ahead of me. However, sometimes fate deals you a funny hand that only makes sense in the light of retrospect. About to graduate from the professional youth team that I had been signed for at thirteen, into the world of the adult game I suffered a fateful injury. Tearing all but one of the ligaments and shattering both cartilages in my right knee. I was in a cast for six months and on crutches for eighteen months. Any shard of hope that I might return to my beloved game drained away as the months rolled by. I needed to come up with a different plan. Football had been my only love. I had taken time out of education to pursue my goal of playing professionally. This combined with undiagnosed dyslexia meant that I had left school without a single qualification to my name.

As my knee slowly healed and the realisation that I would never play again sank in, my passion for the game of football metamorphosed into something new. I threw myself into rehabilitation, learning how to build strength and condition my body in a different way than I had before. I trained. I ate a lot. I gained a lot of weight and muscle. And I became strong. Stronger than I had ever been before. As a sixteen stone powerhouse I was challenged to enter a body building competition the following year. Never one to miss out on a challenge, I dramatically changed my training and my eating plan and lost five stone within a year to drop down to competing weight. But my five foot ten and naturally lean frame was not necessarily built for body building. As my obsession for weights and protein regressed my love for fitness and movement continued to grow. I threw myself into each and every discipline that interested me.

I trained to be a master personal trainer and enthusiastically continued to study for every type of fitness qualification that I could. In the process I became a black belt martial artist, a Pilates instructor, a football coach, an athletic coach and...well the list goes on. In all I have well over seventy sport and fitness qualifications to my name. But somehow it was still not enough. Finally, I took the decision to apply to university and at the grand old age of thirty three I embarked on my undergraduate course in Sport and Exercise Science.

I was diagnosed with dyslexia at University in my first year, which threw some light on why I had been designated into the learning needs class for all my subjects at school. It is one of my proudest achievements that I graduated with a first class honours degree without having any previous schooling qualifications. The passion for my subject shone through, despite all the additional work I needed to do to communicate this passion. I was dedicated and worked extremely hard. My love for the finer details of human movement naturally led me to further my studies by following on with a Masters in Sport and Exercise Biomechanics.

This is really where my problems began. The further I went into the theory of movement; the more I studied and learnt, the more questions I had and the more things became confused for me. From my strong physical and movement based background I understood a lot about how the body really works on an actual physical level. As I studied the finer point of the theories and delved deeper into the world of biomechanics my much loved niche began to present me with some questions. So I allowed the question marks to flow and went deeper down the rabbit hole in search of the answers. Those questions and answers resulted in me writing this book.

Preface

This book is a journey through the questions that I have asked about the established and oft taken for granted laws and rules that underpin how we speak about and define human movement. I started asking questions about why we do things in a certain way and why are we using certain laws or equations to define human movement. At every turn the general response that I received is "because we do." As a scientist, this is not an answer. So as the questions arose I have challenged myself to look for logical explanations, whilst at the same time opening my mind and imagination to the possibility of there being a different answer.

On expressing my views, the one question I get asked the most is "Have you got any research or references to back up what you are saying?" The answer in short, is no. Like most new scientific points of view, I am suggesting a different way, proposing new hypotheses and hopefully the research and 'proof' will follow. Some will go on automatically to assume that if there is no scientific backing then what you are saying is a waste of time. Then there is the other response. The furrowed brow, the calculating look as they way up both sides of the argument before them and the acceptance of open mindedness that allows the possibility of evolution to occur. This type of response is usually from people who understand that the hypothesis comes as the first stage of evolving a new scientific theory. I love conversing, engaging and discussing with the type of person who comes back with the second response as there is the opportunity to journey together.

With people who automatically present with the first response we do not usually have much to say to each other and I find myself feeling disappointed. Why disappointment? Well if you think about it, a lot of the research we carry out in the field of human movement today uses information in some way that has developed from older research papers, which has used even older papers and so it goes on until we find ourselves right back to the roots of a subject. The place where the information was originally birthed, setting the direction and tempo for future evolution of these ideas.

My issue is this. What if, there is the smallest chance, that the very oldest research into this subject has left us with assumptions, findings and mechanical laws that contain inherent flaws, problems and outdated ideologies? Of course, with a science background I completely understand and respect the idea that we need to test, evaluate and prove what is being said. I would be honoured to be involved in any research, development and testing that is able to prove the words in this book and if any one of you comes across a university or research establishment that is able to fund such an endeavour then please give me their phone number!

But currently, as we stand in this place in time, the movement world appears to be fractured into two dualities; those who are so entrenched with the laws and dogmas that have been laid down and accepted in stone as truth and those who are able to see and understand with their own physical being that some of the words, theories and laws we use to describe movement do not provide justice to the complexity of human movement. The second camp are often movement therapists, practitioners and people who are working with the body in a physical capacity on a daily basis.

I am here to challenge. It is not my desire to speak someone else's words, based on the words of their predecessors, or to be told we do things in a certain way or believe certain truths "because we do." My aim is to be a catalyst. A revolutionary in the theoretical world of human movement, who sparks a thought or a feeling in people who are in tune with their own body movement. My aim is to guide you through the history of where we have come from, question the very foundations and shine a light towards the future pathway of how we talk about, define and study human movement. And although currently, at this point in time there is no 'proof' that what I am saying is true, I hope through the deductive reasoning in this book and your understanding of your movement through your own body, a natural conclusion will emerge.

Today, science still speaks of the laws of nature and movement as fixed mechanical laws. Is it not time to question this belief? Do our wonderful, dynamic, elaborate and complex bodies really move like a machine? Is it not time to use organismic control when describing biomechanics? Is it not time to accept that human movement is non-mechanical and free? Is it not time to closely analyse the foundational laws that biomechanics is built upon and ask ourselves the question:

Are these laws correct when describing all human movement?

If you require research and a science laboratories 'proof' that your body works like a machine as the old information on this subject suggests, then I strongly recommend that you do not read this book. Your time and money will be far better spent on a book with repackaged archaic information that likens your body's movement to a lever or some other fixed analogy.

However, if you believe there is more to your movement than meets the biomechanical eye, then let us move on together.

Introduction

Through the coming pages I am planning on taking you on a metaphorical journey. A whistle-stop tour through the foundational laws that biomechanics is built upon. We will pause for thought over the foundational theories that all theoretical movement education is still based upon today and question some of the biggest dogmas in the world of human movement. We will take a look at how history is still effecting the tools, language, diagnostics and conclusions of human biomechanics and most importantly, we will take a look at the possible alternative paths of evolutionary ideas to bring human biomechanics into the twenty first century.

Before we start, please note that throughout the book for simplicity and sense of continuity that I will mainly use the term 'biomechanics' and by this I am referring specifically to human, movement, biomechanics rather than any other branches of the wider term. Also, before we commence I need to make something clear. I am not here to flagrantly dismiss those who have made our understanding of human biomechanics possible thus far – their achievements speak for themselves. But I am here to stand on the shoulders of the giants of our past, in attempt to be part of the never ending and escalating tower of human evolution. I hope to provide additional and alternative information, which I believe can provide a pathway to a different way of thinking.

"Imagination will often carry us to worlds that never were. But without it we go nowhere and without inspiration for future

generations, we will continue to do as we have always done".

-Carl Sagan

Finally, I have attempted to make the material in this book an easy and enjoyable read with succinct chapter 'pit stop' summaries for you to be able to digest the most important messages and threads that run through this book. Following the chapter summaries you will find a section entitled 'thinking cap', where I will present you with a series of questions. These questions are not designed to be taxing, nor are they supposed to be riddles but rather they are simple questions, designed for you to come up with an instant and spontaneous answer. I do not claim to have all the answers and I am hoping that by asking you, the reader, these questions will help to prompt your imagination and encourage you to ask yourself and others more questions.

The thoughts and questions that run throughout the course of this book are intended to provoke a response and I am fully expecting that some people will instantly resonate and like the ideas and some will not. My main hope is that in reading this book you will look behind your current understanding of biomechanics to the foundation of the subject and if you see even a glimmer of misconception that you are not afraid to speak out, join the movement evolution and become an evolved and integral movement practitioner.

Part 1. The Past

Human biomechanics: where has the theory of human movement come from?

A summary of the forefathers of biomechanics

450 – 380 BC	Euclid	Wrote postulates, which contained existing knowledge at the time of geometry and algebra. His geometric laws, which are based on straight lines and right angles are still used today in biomechanical modelling.
1596 – 1650	Rene Descartes	Devised the Cartesian coordinate system, which is a mathematical graph of three dimensions, meeting at right angles, which biomechanics uses today to pinpoint a point of reference (such as a bone, joint or object at a certain speed/angle etc.).
1608 – 1679	Giovanni Alfonso Borelli	Considered to be the first biomechanist, responsible for applying the study of mechanics to the study of human motion and developing the lever principle.
1643 – 1727	Sir Isaac Newton	Defined gravity, the Laws of Motion, calculus and many other physical principles. He is considered the founder of modern science and his principles of motion are what continues to underpin biomechanics today.

1635 – 1703	Robert Hooke	English polymath whose expertise included philosophy and architecture. Devised Hooke's law, which is a spring principle used in biomechanics to represent tissue movement.
1707 – 1783	Leonhard Euler	The pioneering Swiss mathematician and physicist, responsible for important discoveries in varied fields from infinitesimal calculus to graph theory. Euler evolved the Cartesian coordinate system to include rotation.
1827 – 1861	Henry Gray	The English surgeon and anatomist renowned for his dissection work and publication of his book, Gray's Anatomy, which is still widely accepted as a highly acclaimed anatomy textbook. The book was initially illustrated by Gray's friend and colleague Henry Vandyke Carter.

Chapter 1

An introduction to the problem

"A map is not the territory it represents, but if correct, it has a similar structure to the territory, which accounts for its usefulness".

- Alford Korzybski

Do human beings move like robots? Is your movement a predictable, determined, mechanical action? To help me answer these questions I would like to invite you to conjure up a few images in your mind. So just humour me for a minute and play along. Think about Usain Bolt on the running track, Muhammad Ali in the boxing ring, Fred Astaire on the dance floor or Charlie Chaplain's improvised movement in the old black and white movies. Or imagine you are sat in a theatre watching the ballet, a visiting acrobatic circus or contemporary dance collaboration. If you have children think about the movement they make as toddlers; natural, spontaneous movement. And then think about them as they learn to swim, ride their bike, practice martial arts or play football. Also, most of us can think of a time when a human beings movement has left us awe struck and inspired. Whether it be from witnessing an extraordinary feat of acrobatics, admiring the speed and agility of our favourite athlete or being left open mouthed and astounded by a contortionist act.

Is anything about any of these individual's body movements mechanical or robotic? Instinctively, I am hoping that you are shaking your head and answering a clear, resounding "no" in response to this question. How can the beauty, agility and unpredictable nature of human movement be even closely compared to something robotic or mechanical? Even with amazing modern day advancements in twenty first century mechanics, engineers are a long, long way off even coming close to being able to replicate authentic human movement.

So, my next question is this. If our human body in all its complexity does not move like a robot then why do we use a scientific methodology to describe and analyse human movement that compares us to a machine? What is the purpose and usefulness of this?

Most individuals who are 'in to' human movement, all have something in common. Whether their interest lies in:

- Physical training - such as sportspeople, dancers, runners, cyclists, yoga practitioners, Pilate's practitioners, Feldenkrais practitioners or general fitness enthusiasts.

- Anatomy and physiology - such as massage therapists, Rolfers, fascial therapists or Alexandra Technique practitioners.

- Optimising performance - such as personal trainers and functional trainers.

- Rehabilitation, injuries or inefficient movement patterns - such as osteopaths, chiropractors and physiotherapists.

- Education – such as movement, sport or fitness related tutors, teachers and lecturers.

- Movement theory - such as kinesiologists or tensegrity advocates.

All these individuals, whether directly or indirectly; knowingly or unknowingly; independent of their background, discipline or approach to human movement share something of universal importance when it comes to human movement. Biomechanics. The underpinning, often taken for granted scientific laws that define most of the academic understanding, descriptions and analysis concerning human movement.

What is Biomechanics?

As this succinct definition, which is separated into two parts briefly explains:

Bio: meaning life; living organism.

Mechanics: meaning a machine.

Biomechanics, therefore is the mechanical study of the structure and function of a biological system with the attempt to find the forces acting upon the mechanism of a machine. From a biomechanical standpoint this 'machine' can include humans, animals, plants, organs, and cells but for the purpose of this book we are specifically looking at human biomechanics in terms of human movement.

The ideas outlining biomechanical theories and implementation are based upon the following four mechanical principles:

Analytical mechanics – also known as theoretical mechanics, this branch of mechanics looks at scalar properties (physical quantity) of motion as opposed to Newtonian mechanics that looks at vector properties (quantity and direction). Using system constraints the degrees of freedom are limited and coordinate reduced to solve the problem of motion. Analytical mechanics does not take into account new physics.

Applied mechanics - this is a branch of the physical sciences that deals with the practical application of classical mechanics, bridging the gap between physical theory and its application. A practitioner of this discipline is known as a mechanician and is involved in examining the response of isolated bodies or systems to external forces. Much of modern engineering mechanics is based on Sir Isaac Newton's laws of motion. Newtonian mechanics is widely known as classical mechanics, which is one of the oldest and largest subjects in science, engineering and technology. Classical mechanics was originally meant to be used in the field of engineering mechanics but it also provided a foundation from which biomechanics has sprung from.

Statistical mechanics - is a branch of mathematical mechanics that studies the average behaviour of a mechanical system, when the true state of the system is uncertain. The objective of statistical mechanics is to develop and employ mathematical models, theories and/or hypotheses to solve a question. The process of measurement is central to quantitative research because it provides the fundamental connection between small pieces of information with the aim of bridging the disconnection between the laws of mechanics and the reality of the organism human. This is achieved by making deductions about the whole or future based upon individual components of a system. It also uses simple mathematics by rejecting complex data, which does not operate in predicable ways. Statistical mechanics then attempts to find patterns, symmetry, regulatory and relationships among regulated numbers.

Computational mechanics - this discipline is concerned with the use of computational methods to represents mechanical principles. This branch is concerned with constructing mathematical models, quantitative analysis techniques and using computers to analyse and solve biomechanical problems.

Classical mechanics

Classical mechanics is the foundation of all mechanical principles and from the ideas outlined in the classical mechanical model, the applied and computational mechanical principles evolved. There are various branches of classical mechanics that we need to understand as we delve further into the foundation of biomechanics, including:

Rigid-body dynamics – this studies the movement of interconnected bodies under the action of external forces, assuming that the objects under investigation are perfectly rigid; meaning that no part will deform, bend or stretch once forces are applied. This assumption simplifies the analysis procedure by reducing the variables.

Statics – is concerned with the analysis of loads (force) on physical systems in static equilibrium.

Dynamics - is concerned with the study of forces and torques and their effect on motion.

Kinematics – based on geometry, this describes the motion of points, bodies (objects) and systems of bodies (groups of objects) without consideration of the causes of motion.

Kinetics - is concerned with the relationship between the motion of bodies and its causes, namely forces. Kinetics is based on mathematics and classical mechanics.

The interconnection of these branches of classical mechanics are represented in figure 1 below. This shows that statics, dynamics, kinematics and kinetics have all evolved based upon rigid body dynamics, which we will examine in more detail later on.

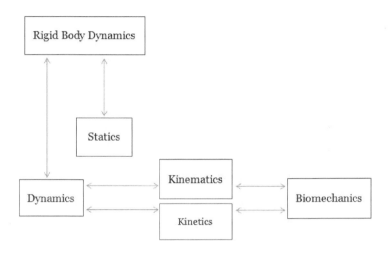

Figure 1

The human body as a machine – where did this idea come from?

According to human biomechanics, man is made and moves like a machine. I am hoping the last time you looked in the mirror your reflection didn't look anything like a robot or tin person? I thought not. There is quite a lot of obvious differences between your human body and a machine, which can be defined as an often motorized tool; containing one or more parts that uses mechanical, chemical, thermal or electrical energy to perform a task.

There are six types of simple machine:

- Lever

- Wheel and axle

- Pulley

- Inclined plane

- Wedge

- Screw

Any of these simple machines uses a single applied force to do work against a single load force. Ignoring friction losses, the work performed is equal to the work produced. These simple machines are isolated parts or building blocks, which can then be connected together with rigid links to create a more complex machine.

This idea of small isolated parts being connected together to form a more complex machine is the analogy used in biomechanics to represent the human body. There are two mechanistic frameworks that provided biomechanics with the foundational understanding that the body is a machine. Firstly, the universal mechanism and secondly, the anthropic mechanism.

The universal mechanism describes celestial and terrestrial bodies (space and earth), which is based around materialism and reductionism of the universe into simplistic mechanical principles. The concept of the universal mechanism uses Euclid's theory that nature can be described from a mathematical set of shapes, which provided those who believed in a mechanistic view that all natural phenomenon could eventually be explained in terms of mechanical laws.

The anthropic mechanism used the ideas and mathematics from the universal mechanism to describe what was happening upon the earth. When the anthropic mechanistic idea was devised, it was believed that both the body and the mind were formed of individual parts or simple machines. The ideas around anthropic mechanism is deeply indoctrinated and is still the foundation for biomechanics today.

Both, universal and anthropic mechanisms are external laws, which are deterministic; meaning that they follow a set standard of rigid rules that do not change. Biomechanics uses information from both universal and anthropic mechanisms to mathematically equate man's movement based upon simplistic and mechanistic theories.

The organismic human

"The whole is greater than the sum of its parts."

Aristotle

Today, biomechanics is still using anthropic and universal mechanics, which are over 5,000 year old ideologies. Because biomechanics is rooted in these theories, the very underpinning essence of this science assumes that our human body is a machine. Consequently, all of the scientific data involving human movement is associated with this belief. Is this theory correct? We know that the "map is not the territory" but surely there must be a more accurate map than the reductionist one we are currently holding in our hands.

The problems with viewing the body through this mechanistic looking glass are numerous. We know that machines are man-made, whereas the human organism is morphogenetic and infinitely more complex than any man built systems. One of the most vital differences between organisms and machines is to be found in the purposiveness of the systems. Both organisms and machines operate towards the attainment of a particular end, with their purposiveness being that of a completely different kind. A machine is extrinsically purposive because it operates towards an end that is external to itself, whereas an organism is intrinsic in its design.

A machine does not serve its own interests but those of its maker or user. In contrast, an organism acts on its own behalf, towards its own ends. Its design is internal, arising from within, and serving no other purpose than to maintain its own organization. A machine is also organized, of course, given that the operation of each part is dependent on it being properly arranged with respect to every other part and to the system as a whole. But in an organism, the parts are not just there for the sake of each other, but they also produce each other, repair each other and generally exist by means of one another. Organisms, unlike machines, are not only organized but are also self-organizing and self-reproducing systems. From a mechanistic approach, with isolated parts attempting to create a 'whole' we are left with inherent separateness. True interaction between the parts is an impossibility as each part performs in isolation as its own 'whole'.

In addition, organisms have an autonomous self; the phenomena of self-formation, self-regeneration, self-preservation and self-repair are all characteristics of the internal dynamics of living systems. Machines, on the other hand, lack an autonomous self; their means of production reside outside of themselves, demanding outside intervention not just for their construction but also for their maintenance. Indeed, for the sustained operation of a machine, an external agent is required to determine when defective components need to be repaired or replaced and to carry them out in a timely fashion. In an organism, all of these processes are carried out from within. Therefore, confronted with a machine, one is perfectly justified in inferring the existence of an external creator responsible for producing it in accordance to a preconceived plan or design.

Dynamic complex biological systems, including the human body and the production of human movement, have the tendency to spontaneously self-organize themselves to produce intricate patterns. The process of self-organization is the foundation of all living systems and is fundamentally associated with survival and evolution. The mechanistic approach of isolated parts, joined together to make up the whole cannot in reality self-organise, as within the mechanistic view, self-organisation would only effect the isolated parts. An organism however, will self-organise as a whole irrespective of the parts. The problem is that biomechanics is trying to explain biological life by means of mechanical ideology. However, unlike the predictability found in a mechanical system, self-organizing systems are non-predictable in nature.

Quantitative vs qualitative

The preceding sections have introduced the outline of the problems associated with using a mechanistic model when analysing a complex, bio or living system such as the human body. So why has this view not been approached, questioned or challenged before now? I believe one of the main reasons is because the mechanistic view of the world can at a rudimentary, simplistic level be mathematically understood. This enables the production of some empirical evidence, which helps to quantify the nature of life. Also, of course to challenge history and ideas that have evolved thus far takes a process of transformation. A quantum shift in education, understanding and belief.

However, just because the glorious and unpredictable nature of the human body makes it difficult to analyse from a mathematical point of view does not mean that there is not a better way. It is this unpredictability that presents a problem to the analysis of true human movement, as it is near impossible to mathematically equate the inherent random nature. So if the quantitative data is problematic, perhaps we need to look more closely at the qualitative element of analysis. Of course, there are many skilled practitioners of all disciplines that use a more qualitative approach with kinesiology at the most experiential end. Quantitative mathematics has its place, as does qualitative research but at the moment there is a huge cross wire in this area of understanding, which we will examine more thoroughly in section two.

Ultimately, I propose that for us to bring our understanding of the human body to a deeper, more profound level, we need to evolve some of the oldest foundations that our current knowledge has been built upon.

Who cares?

I strongly believe that the biomechanical view of the human body is outdated. By questioning the foundations of a subject many of us take for granted we stand a chance of evolving our understanding and coming up with a working model that will enhance many people's understanding as well as their practice and results.

Currently, in the movement world from education through to practitioners, the theory behind the art of practice is being spread far and wide without a full understanding of the origins of the subject. There are many practitioners who are passing on their educational understanding of the theory behind their work, even though the reality is the words they are using are often at complete odds with their findings in clinical practice. So when we are talking about the theory of movement like this, it is not only paramount to enhance people's perceived understanding of the subject but it also has repercussions for implementation and practice.

The main areas that biomechanics influences on a far reaching level are:

- Improving performance.

- Preventing and treating injuries and postural related pain.

- Designing equipment to make movement easier for the human organism.

So if you are involved in any of the above then it is highly probably that you use the principles of biomechanics on a regular basis. Taking this into consideration, if you are using mechanical principles to analyse, treat, support your views or reach a desired goal then any information and subsequent prescriptions may contain inherent flaws, inaccuracies and may not be providing the most effective way of reaching a desired outcome.

Essentially, what I am talking about here is evolving our current thinking, models and way of talking about, analysing and treating human movement to fit in with twenty first century scientific understanding.

Pit Stop Summary

- Biomechanics is based on a mechanistic view of the body with an underlying belief that the body is made up of the 6 simple machines in various combinations, in any of its systems.

- Biomechanics uses information obtained from universal mechanistic views. This theory originated from observations about space, with the parallel being drawn between occurrences happening on a celestial level and occurrences happening on earth.

- Biomechanics uses the information obtained from the anthropic mechanism, which was built upon the simplified constant of numbers being generated that reduced the complex and unpredictable to something more predictable and quantifiable.

Hopefully, from reading this first chapter you will agree that there are some obvious differences between a mechanistic system and an organismic system. Table 1 below highlights some fundamental differences. As you read through ask yourself, which column do you fall into if considering your own human body in context with the variables?

Variable	Organism/ Bio	Biomechanics/Machine
Location	Intrinsic	Extrinsic
Identity	Internally generated	Externally generated
Operation	Transitional	Isolated
Attribution	Interdependent	Dependent
Determinism	Whole	Parts
Genesis	Self-producing	Created by an agent/ man
Product	Evolution by nature	Designed by man
Behaviour	Flexible/adaptive	Fixed /rigid
Tested	Non math models	Math models

Outcome	Non Predicable and non-determined	Predicable and deterministic
Status	Alive	Dead

Table 1 – Difference between an organism and a machine.

Thinking cap

NB: Remember this Thinking Cap section contains straight forward questions. I am not trying to catch you out. As you read the questions just use your common sense to give a spontaneous answer. These are the basics and I am sure you as the reader can think of more questions that highlight the issues we face by continuing to use biomechanics, without opening up alternative movement theory possibilities.

1. Do you move, think, feel, act and live like a machine?

2. Do you think a machine can replicate your human movement?

3. Do you think your skeleton, muscles fascia, blood, ligaments etc. operate according to mechanistic logic?

4. Does using machine science based on innate objects truly represent the human organism?

5. Remember, biomechanics is based on a mechanistic view of the body that has evolved from universal and anthropic mechanics. Does this logic provide an accurate map to describe the workings of the human organism?

6. According to mechanistic theory and human biomechanics our body is like a machine. If this were true and we are robot like then who created and maintains the machine?

Chapter 2

Are we lines and shapes?

"The laws of nature are but the mathematical thoughts of God".

- Euclid

The Greek mathematician, Euclid of Alexandria (c.450-380 BCE) is often referred to as the "Father of Geometry". His most famous work is the *Elements*, a thirteen-volume treatise that systematically organized all of the existing knowledge of number theory, algebra and geometry that had been developed up until that time. Euclidean geometry is an axiomatic system, in which all theorems (true statements) are derived from a small number of axioms.

Near the beginning of the first book of the *Elements*, Euclid defined the following five postulates:

1. *"To draw a straight line from any point to any point."*

2. *"To produce [extend] a finite straight line continuously in a straight line."*

3. *"To describe a circle with any centre and distance [radius]."*

4.   *"That all right angles are equal to one another."*

5.   *The parallel postulate: "That, if a straight line falling on two straight lines make the interior angles on the same side less than two right angles, the two straight lines, if produced indefinitely, meet on that side on which are the angles less than the two right angles."*

The *Elements* also include the following five **axioms** or common notions:

1.   *Things which equal the same thing also equal one another.*

2.   *If equals are added to equals, then the wholes are equal.*

3.   *If equals are subtracted from equals, then the remainders are equal.*

4.   *Things which coincide with one another equal one another.*

5.   *The whole is greater than the part.*

Essentially, these five axioms above specifically describe plane geometry. A plane is a two dimensional, flat surface without thickness. A plane can be thought of as x and y.

In mathematics, a plane can be described as a flat, two-dimensional surface.

Euclid believed that his axioms were self-evident statements about physical reality. They were then used as a foundation in describing the shape and design of the universe and all that inhibits it. These Euclidean 'laws of nature' provided a theory that God had built the universe based upon a simple geometrical shape and this theory was later used to offer a mathematical solution to God's design.

Euclidian geometry never made use of numbers or mathematics to measure length, angle or area but rather Euclid evolved his system using the following stages:

1. Initially, Euclid used dots in space to represent a position, which had zero dimensions.

2. He then joined these dots up with straight lines, which gave him one dimension.

3. He then designed shapes based around these joint up lines with the foundational shapes being a triangle, square and pentagon. These shapes provided a two dimensional model.

4. Finally, Euclid wanted to create a three dimensional model so he created five platonic solids: tetrahedron, octahedron, cube, icosahedron and dodecahedron. These solids were in fact still two dimensional as they were drawings rather than models. Euclid believed that these five platonic shapes represented all under Gods creation.

Euclidian shapes are fixed; rigid; constant; with straight lines; fixed angles and are predictable. Non-Euclidian geometry on the other hand is curved; changes shape; is adaptive; is without angles and can be unpredictable. More to come on this later!

How does Biomechanics use Euclidean geometry?

Euclidean geometry is the foundation for all biomechanical modelling of the human organism. In turn, this is the basis which kinesiology (the study of movement) and biological structures were based upon whenever movement was represented. The understanding of Euclidean geometry forms the foundation for all biomechanical computations, research, experiments, education, teaching and more importantly ongoing research into the area of human movement. So if this very foundation of Euclidean geometry is a poor parallel or an outdated way of looking at, understanding and analysing the human body and human movement, where does that leave us with regards to the study of human movement?

All of the current three-dimensional video analysis used in biomechanics to represent the human body in space, uses Euclidian geometry in the following ways:

1. **To provide a box to measure movement in** – a square is used to box in the movement being recorded, which is known as a video analysis box. This Euclidian geometric shape is then synced with Descartes three dimensional coordinate system, alongside Newtonian mathematics.

2. **It uses straight lines and points** – represented by a free-body diagram, which is a stick man representation and a one dimensional model.

3. **The skeletal system is represented by these free-body diagrams** - we will find out more later, regarding distance, force, angles, time and representation in space being based upon a lever system.

4. **To represent joints** – when a joint is looked at in more depth in modern biomechanics it is still represented as a Euclidian shape of triangles and squares.

Euclidian platonic solids and vectors

In modern human biomechanics, major areas of the body such as the pelvis, spine and head are represented by a classical Euclidian geometrical shape such as a triangle, rectangle, square or circle and alternative models represented by a platonic solids. Pythagoras theorem is the underlying foundation of vectors. This theory states that the square of the hypotenuse (the side opposite the right angle) is equal to the sum of the squares of the other two sides. However, at the time Pythagoras theorem was not expressed in mathematics as an equation, this came later through algebra.

Euclidian geometry is used in biomechanics as the representation of fixed lines and perfectly symmetrical shapes.

In Euclidean geometry a vector represents the position of a point (P) in space in relation to an arbitrary reference origin (O). Usually denoted by x, y or z, it corresponds to the straight line distance from O to P, which is the foundation of analytic geometry. Or more simply put the lines between point a) and point b) are known as a vector and these straight line vectors allow biomechanists to calculate the direction of force and the magnitude (size) of force.

The Euclidian idea of using lines, points, circles and solids to represent the natural world provided Rene Descartes the foundation to develop analytic geometry by adding algebra to Euclidean geometry. Vectors (a line) form the basis of analytic geometry or Cartesian geometry, which describes any point in three-dimensional space by means of three coordinates. Three coordinate axis are given, usually each perpendicular to the other two at the origin and are usually labelled x, y, and z. Straight lines are represented as constant, predictable and formulated equations, based upon plane geometry. This is the Cartesian coordinate system, which will be discussed in more depth later in this book.

Rigid Bodies

A major aspect to Euclid's ideas was that of the rigid body. He felt that geometry was built upon shapes that are solid, symmetrical and predictable. This concept in physics is an idealization of a solid body, with given distances between two different points being constant, without deformation being taken into account.

A rigid body can be defined by these points:

1. A mass point system joined together to form links.

2. A body with a continuous mass distribution, with an unchanging shape.

3. When a rigid body moves the distance between any two points in a rigid body remains constant, regardless of the exertion of external forces.

4. Rigid bodies are in balance, fixed and symmetrical at all times.

From rigid body geometry, kinematics and kinetics have evolved, which are all keystones of modern human biomechanics.

So what's the problem?

The world of biomechanics is a world of estimations, predictions and guesswork achieved from applying simplistic models, originally intended for static, non-living objects, based in symmetrical shapes in an attempt to find a matching mathematical number.

Biomechanics uses a synthetic approach, dealing with abstract geometric objects that are assumed to satisfy certain geometrical properties provided by the Euclidian axioms and solids, which are based upon Pythagoras theorem. To calculate force in biomechanics a Euclidian geometrical shape and trigonometry are used. Both of these have to have a fixed angle and trigonometry uses a right angle triangle. This is the idea that thee sides of a right angled triangle are related and can represent all movement and all biological tissue. In order to take the point zero dimensions and add the line dimensions of a plane to it in the form of a triangle, which combined forms the platonic solids outlined by Euclidean, there must be no curvature or deformation to any shape. In any attempt to take this two dimensional picture representation and make a three dimensional object there must be no curvature or deformation to the object; this means that any of the parts that make up the object must be a rigid body. If this was the case everything would be symmetrical and balanced and nothing would move!

Euclidian geometry is based on axioms and postulates, which then became solid shapes and fixed lines, to represent objects. These were originally intended to be used for innate objects, based on a flat surface designed upon paper where the object is static, rigid and constant. This method then forms the foundation for biomechanical computer modelling and free body diagrams, which provides a simplistic representation of human movement in the form of a stick figure. To do this biomechanics uses free body diagrams .These stick man representations of the full biological system are simplified to straight lines of Euclidean geometry, with predetermined angles representing joints; which are fixed, non-deforming and constant. A second problem is the use of vectors, which are a main biomechanical principle. These one dimensional, single joint lines stop at points representing direction and magnitude. The forces conducted through a vector are not connected to an overall system. Vectors have forces that are not connected to a system. Does this sound like the human organism and its movement? In biomechanics examples are a straight line representing a bone and a dot for a joint.

It is interesting to note that mechanical engineering, which is based and designed upon non-living elements of a man made machine, structure or parts of a machine, has moved on from the concept of a rigid body. Engineers have acknowledged that no object can be a rigid body in real life. Therefore, they have introduced the concept of a resistant body, which means that the object does not deform for the purpose for which it was made. So a table is a resistant body, meaning it is a rigid body for the purpose for which it was made but if a certain amount of pressure is applied to the table it will not remain rigid as it was not designed to take this force into consideration. So mechanical engineering has addressed this issue of rigid bodies to use a more realistic alternative in engineering problems. Biomechanics on the other hand still has rigid bodies at its foundation.

Pit Stop Summary

- Biomechanics uses free body diagrams, three dimensional coordinates (more about this in the next chapter) and vector analysis as the foundation for assessing and analysing body position, forces moving through the body and movement.

- This is all based upon Euclidean geometry of axioms and solids, which was designed upon the right hand rule of a tringle by Pythagoras. In order to fulfil the requirements there will only be straight lines with and without angles and when combined into a solid, the points are attached by a joint with the vector forces being isolated and discontinuous.

Thinking cap

NB: Remember this Thinking Cap section contains straight forward questions. I am not trying to catch you out. As you read the questions just use your common sense to give a spontaneous answer. These are the basics and I am sure you as the reader can think of more questions that highlight the issues we face by continuing to use biomechanics, without opening up alternative movement theory possibilities.

This thinking cap is based around the defined Euclidian postulates, axioms and principles of a rigid body. All of these underpin Euclidian geometry and are still used in modern biomechanics today. But how applicable are these rules and principles when looking at the body as an organism? Answer the questions for yourself and see what you think...

Postulates

Postulate 1 - "To draw a straight line from any point to any point."

Postulate 2 – "To produce (extend) a finite straight line continuously in a straight line." Or in other words: a finite straight line can be extended continuously in a straight line or any straight

37

line segment can be extended indefinitely in a straight line.

Postulate 3 - "To describe a circle with any centre and distance [radius]." Or in other words: a circle can be formed with any centre and distance (radius) or given any straight line segment, a circle can be drawn having the segment as radius and one endpoint as centre.

Postulate 4 - "That all right angles are equal to one another." Or in other words: All right angles are congruent or equal to one another.

Postulate 5 - The parallel postulate: "That, if a straight line falling on two straight lines make the interior angles on the same side less than two right angles, the two straight lines, if produced indefinitely, meet on that side on which are the angles less than the two right angles." Or in other words: if two lines are drawn which intersect a third in such a way that the sum of the inner angles on one side is less than two right angles, then the two lines inevitably must intersect each other on that side if extended far enough.

Questions:

1) Is anything in the human body ever in a completely straight line?

2) Is movement ever in a completely straight line?

3) Do defined points exist in the body when looking at human movement or is the body interconnected?

4) Where do two parallel straight lines ever meet in the body?

5) If a line can go on continuously in a straight line then is it moving always in a linear way?

6) Where in nature and evolution does this ever occur?

7) Where are there every 100% symmetrical objects in nature?

8) If everything is always symmetrical then it is always in balance, where is there 100% balance in nature?

9) Where is there a true right angle that represents a living entity in nature and the human organism?

10) Where in nature and humans is there anything that is equal and exactly the same?

11) Where in nature and humans does the fifth postulate occur?

Axioms

"Things which equal the same thing also equal one another."

"If equals are added to equals, then the wholes are equal."

"If equals are subtracted from equals, the remainders are equal."

"Things which coincide with one another equal one another."

"The whole is greater than the part."

Questions:

1) Where and when are two things ever exactly equal in the human body?

2) Where and when are two things exactly equal in the human body, once things have been added or taken away?

3) Where do things ever stay the same?

4) Where is there ever pure balance?

5) Are all objects the same?

6) Where does anything that coincides or touches in the human body become equal?

7) "The whole is greater than the part." This is the only axiom which suggests that the parts of something are not as strong as the whole. A suggestion of a self-organising element, which I completely agree with.

Rigid bodies

Points that define a rigid body:

- A mass point system joined together to form links.

- A body with a continuous mass distribution, with an unchanging shape.

- When a rigid body moves the distance between any two points in a rigid body remains constant, regardless of the exertion of external forces.

- Rigid bodies are in balance, fixed and symmetrical at all times.

Questions:

1) Is there such a thing as an isolated, independent point in the human body?

2) Where is there a continuous, unchanging distribution and shape in the human body?

3) Everything in the human body changes shape, everything is non-symmetrical and chaotic. It is interesting to note that whilst in classical mechanics a rigid body is defined as a continuous mass distribution, in quantum mechanics a rigid body is usually defined as a collection of point masses.

4) Where in the human body is anything ever rigid or solid?

5) If force is applied to the body would it deform?

6) How can rigid bodies take deformation into account?

7) If everything is the human body was in balance, static and symmetrical would movement and evolution ever occur?

8) Is human movement predictable and repeatable?

Chapter 3

Is our movement dot-to-dot?

"Perfect numbers like perfect men are very rare".

- Rene Descartes

The French mathematician, scientist and philosopher, Rene Descartes (1596 - 1650) is often referred to as the father of modern philosophy. Along with his widely studied and acclaimed philosophical writings, Descartes also played a key part in the scientific revolution and he is thought of as the father of analytical geometry; the connection between algebra and geometry. Descartes created a form of algebra that allowed him to represent Euclid's dots, lines and shapes mathematically in the form of x, y and z axes. Descartes mathematical influence has had great and lasting impact and of particular interest to this book, his Cartesian coordinate system is still used in modern human biomechanics today.

Descartes believed that the human body worked like a machine and could be mapped in space. He advocated that the individual parts and different pieces of the human machine were like a clockwork mechanism and the overall working of the machine could be understood by taking its pieces a part and studying them, before putting them back together to see the larger picture. This was much like the lever systems principle outlined by Borelli, with the clockwork mechanism of mankind being closely related to a simple machine. It is important to remember that this concept at the time had the underlying belief that these simple machines were made by God and followed the natural laws of physics based upon Euclidean geometry.

From Descartes philosophical works he is renowned for devising three laws of nature, which stated:

Law 1. *Each thing, in so far as it is simple and undivided, always remains in the same state, as far as it can, and never changes except as a result of external causes...Hence we must conclude that what is in motion always, so far as it can, continues to move.* (*Principles* Part II, art. 37)

- Meaning each thing tries to remain in the same state. So nothing changes in size, shape or weight; nothing is deformable and everything is rigid.

Law 2. Every piece of matter, considered in itself, always tends to continue moving, not in any oblique path but only in a straight line. (Principles Part II, art. 39)

- So, all movement is along straight lines.

Law 3. When a moving body collides with another, if its power of continuing in a straight line is less than the resistance of the other body, it is deflected so that, while the quantity of motion is retained, the direction is altered; but if its power of continuing is greater than the resistance of the other body, it carries that body along with it, and loses a quantity of motion equal to that which it imparts to the other body. (Principles Part II, art. 40)

So, when a body comes into contact with another body the combined motion remains the same and energy cannot move from one thing to another.

Interestingly, these three laws of nature later became some of the ideas that formed Newton's laws of motion, which are the foundations of modern biomechanics in terms of quantifying human movement.

The Cartesian coordinate system

The coordinate system designed by Descartes is still used in biomechanics today. It shows a fixed point of reference in a particular plane that can be mathematically equated. Descartes achieved a three dimensional coordinate system by following these stages:

1. Euclid was interested in the shape itself and not how or where it was represented in space. Whereas Descartes wanted to find an object in space and time. He did this initially with a two dimensional model, which was a combination of two, one-dimensional axis', positioned at 90 degrees to one another. This allowed him to represent

an object as a dot (a zero dimensional object) in time and space to create a two dimensional model.

2. The inclusion of a shape within his representation of an object in space and time was to add an additional one dimensional line, which dissected the middle of the two dimensional lines at an angle. This gave Descartes x, y and z. So essentially, the Descartes coordinate system is three, one-dimensional axes layered on top of each other to create a three-dimensional model.

For Descartes to justify his ideas about representing nature within a coordinate system he had to find a set of mathematical principles to justify his system. So he took Euclidian geometry and devised analytical geometry, which included the mathematical principles of algebra. This provided Descartes with a quantifiable system and the mathematics to justify his beliefs about the coordinate system. In simple terms a mathematical system to justify man-made shapes.

How is the Cartesian coordinate system used in biomechanics today?

The video software packages used to analyse human movement in modern biomechanics utilises the three dimensional coordinate system. The software analysis packages basically work by using dots placed on the human form (zero dimensions) with lines (one dimensions) joining these dots up, to create a stick figure diagram to analyse and represent human movement.

During biomechanical analysis dots or markers are placed on the human body. For example, on the elbow, the shoulder and the wrist. These points are then joined with lines to represent the arm. So this computer modelling takes a zero dimensional dot or marker, joins it into a line to provide a one dimensional figure, which is then graphed in accordance with the Cartesian coordinate system. This graphing process provides three, one-dimensional lines (x, y, z) placed at 90 degrees to each other to represent three dimensions.

The image that is recorded of human movement by the software package is then mathematically graphed to find a constant set of numbers representing speed, distance and time that allows for estimations to be made to predict future movements. For these experiments to occur the movement carried out within the study will be modified by the software in ways that will take out any inconsistencies or irregularity that all human movement inherently has; to create an average, constant and deterministic movement that can be represented by a number. In other words human movement is reduced and simplified to a machine principle.

What about rotation?

A century after Descartes, Leonard Euler (1707 – 1783), a Swiss mathematician, engineer and physicist, modified the original Cartesian coordinate system by taking the three linear coordinates (side to side, up and down, forward and backward) and applied a second set of three dimensional coordinates but this time rotational. Euler used both Descartes and Newtonian mathematics to justify his view. Rather than the box format that Descartes used, Euler attempted to use a spherical coordinate system, which incorporated a rotational element to the original coordinate system and resulted in a more three dimensional representation. However, Euler still used Newton's laws within his mathematics. This resulted in a full three dimensional pictorial representation but using three, one dimensional lines (more about Newton's laws of motion in the next chapter).

In spite of this, Euler's upgraded coordinate system provided what should be a coordinate system based on six factors – forward and back, side to side, up and down, heave, sway and roll. These six factors are what engineers use today and are termed as the 'six degrees of freedom'. The thing to remember is these six degrees of freedom are still based upon two laws to describe the motion of a rigid body, relative to an inertial reference frame.

The first law describes how applied forces change the velocity of the centre of mass of a rigid body. The second law describes how the change in angular momentum of a rigid body is influenced by the moment of the applied force and any attachments to other bodies an object may have. These laws were written for bodies of fixed matter. Meaning that the body must be composed of a fixed amount and type of matter that does not change shape and must be free from other forces, just like the Cartesian model.

Euler's addition of rotation to Descartes linear model still takes the positions in accordance with the linear model rather than independently from it. So the linear model is still the reference frame for any rotation that occurs. Secondly, the rotations that do occur are still within a constant time, speed and distance frame and must still be in association with a rigid object and purely symmetrical rotations.

So what is the full three dimensional coordinate system?

The position of a rigid body in a three dimensional coordinate system is defined by the rigid transformation, of either translation (straight) or rotational (round). This relates to the degree of freedom of a system which can be viewed as the minimum number of coordinates required to specify a configuration. Applying this definition, we have six in total which correlates to Euler's coordinate system.

The following are the six degrees of freedom that are taken

from a three dimensional coordinate system:

Translation -

1. Moving up and down (heaving).

2. Moving left and right (swaying).

3. Moving forward and backward (surging).

Rotation -

4. Tilts forward and backward (pitching).

5. Swivels left and right (yawing).

6. Pivots side to side (rolling).

The Cartesian coordinate system uses either:

1) A point which has zero dimensions (these dots can be the dots used on a free body diagram).

2) A line which has one dimension (these lines can be the lines used on a stick man diagram).

3) A flat shape which has two dimensions (e.g. a triangle drawn on a piece of paper).

Descartes evolved his coordinate system by using one dimensional Euclidian geometry, a straight line and adding a second one dimensional line, which gave two dimensions but based on one dimensional geometry. These lines were then placed at right angles to each other. He then added a third one dimensional line, which was placed at a right angle to the first two straight lines, each being perpendicular to the other, which resulted in three dimensions. This mathematics was the birth of algebra and based upon Euclidean geometry and his axioms. The development of the Cartesian coordinate system would go on to play an intrinsic role in the development of calculus by Sir Isaac Newton.

A second coordinate system is occasionally used in biomechanics called a polar coordinate system, which is a mathematical two-dimensional coordinate system where each point on a plane is determined by a distance from a reference point and an angle from a reference direction. Polar coordinates provide a method of rendering graphs and indicating the positions of points on a two-dimensional flat surface and are employed in mathematics, physics, engineering, navigation, robotics and other sciences to find a set of symmetrically isolated positions, circles or sections of circles. All of the problems associated with the Cartesian coordinate system apply exactly to the polar coordinate system as well, so it is not a viable alternative.

So what's the problem?

Biomechanics attempts to create a three dimensional inanimate solid, to represent the human body. However, the Cartesian coordinate system is based on zero dimensions in the form of dots. These dots are then joined together to form lines providing one dimension. These lines are then joined together to create a shape providing two dimensions. A computer package then proceeds to 'fills in the blanks' to provide an estimate and a mathematical predication to create a three dimensional image of a solid.

In the attempt to be able to quantify a position or point in space, biomechanics uses the coordinate system. As I have already mentioned the Cartesian system offered by Descartes used the Euclidean axioms and geometry of a line and solid to represent three dimensions. This means that the Cartesian system was built up of three single dimensions layered on top of each other, with a zero dimensional dot as the starting point, attempting to represent a three dimensional solid shape. Modern biomechanical analysis computer software packages reproduces this attempt to analyse a three dimensional shape (the human body) by using zero-dimensional dots in the form of a free body diagram, built up into a one dimensional image using a stick figure.

Another problem with the Descartes coordinate system is that he never did manage to come up with a defining or finalised mathematical equation to back up his system. The coordinate system represents a point in time with different references (time/speed etc.). However, this was highly problematic as Descartes was unable to replicate the same two points on a graph twice. Due to the unpredictable and random nature he was unable to quantify a precise number that represents everything. So although his original coordinate system provided a reference frame, due to the unpredictable nature of the reference points he was working with he was unable to mathematically equate these positions. Without the definitive numbers associated with the coordinate system it was limited to finding a fixed point in time of a particular object or part of an object based on distance, speed and time (x, y and z). Therefore, this is an unrealistic model when trying to graph the complexity of the full cascade of human movement, within a real time-frame. It is also important to remember that during the era that Descartes was working the measurement of time was recorded with instruments such as a sand based timing device, which is vastly different to our scientific measures we would use today.

Ultimately, the problem is that biomechanics is only using zero-dimensional markers in the form of dots, which is a point of reference to represents the whole object being studied within a certain time frame. These restrictions make it far simpler to mathematically equate and repeat as well as predicting patterns of likely outcomes. The coordinate system is essentially attempting to be a three dimensional model based on one dimensional, linear geometry

It is also important to remember that during the time that Descartes was working, the church was a powerful force overseeing all scientific, philosophical and mathematical statements, which all had to conform to the religious views of the ruling monarch of the time. All physical design at the time was explained as mechanical and through deterministic mathematics set out by God. Descartes came from a dualistic approach, which was the favoured belief system of the time, meaning he believed the body and mind were separate entities and that both worked on mechanistic principles. His three laws of nature that he hypothesised are based upon the body and mind being separate mechanical systems.

Pit Stop Summary

Descartes believed that the body was a dualistic machine made up of isolated parts that had been created by God and adhered to natural laws of physics in accordance with Euclidian geometry.

- Descartes three laws of nature preceded Newton's three laws of motion and stated that:

    1) Each thing tries to remain in the same state. So nothing changes in size, shape or weight; nothing is deformable and everything is rigid.

    2) All movement is along straight lines.

    3) When a body comes into contact with another body, the combined motion remains the same and energy cannot move from one thing to another.

- The Descartes coordinate system was devised by layering three, one-dimensional elements together to give a three-dimensional model to allow him to graph an object in space and time.

- Descartes devised analytical geometry, to provide a mathematical system to justify Euclidian geometry.

- In the next century Euler added rotation to Descartes coordinate model, which resulted in six degrees of freedom, rather than three.

- Descartes coordinate system is still used in modern biomechanical software packages to isolate and reduce movement down to a linear one/two dimensional stick figure.

- Euler's coordinate system, which shows an upgraded six degrees of freedom rather than three degrees of freedom like in Descartes model, is used today in engineering but is not used or embraced by the biomechanical community.

Thinking Cap

NB: Remember this Thinking Cap section contains straight forward questions. I am not trying to catch you out. As you read the questions just use your common sense to give a spontaneous answer. These are the basics and I am sure you as the reader can think of more questions that highlight the issues we face by continuing to use biomechanics, without opening up alternative movement theory possibilities.

1) If Euclidean geometry is problematic when looking at the human body does this not make further systems based upon this view also a problem?

2) Is using single line (linear) geometry a true representation of any living structure?

3) By using linear mathematics can we hope to realistically represent a multi-dimensional human organism and its movement?

4) By using the principles of rigid bodies can we hope to realistically represent the human organism and its movement?

5) Is the human organism and its movement ever at a right angle?

6) Does the human organism and its movement ever change shape?

7) Does the human organism and its movement move in straight lines?

8) Does the human organism and its movement ever change its energy from one form to another?

9) If there were three linear coordinates in Descartes system and three rotational movements in Euler's updated coordinate system then why are biomechanics still only using three – two from Descartes and one from Euler and not six?

10) There are six degree of freedom but only two points? Does the human organism and its movement have more than two points interacting at once?

Chapter 4

Are we just levers?

"No sensible person will deny that the works of Nature are in the highest degree simple, necessary and as economical as possible. Therefore machines devised by mankind will doubtlessly likewise attain most success if they are as far as possible modelled on works of Nature".

- Giovanni Alfonso Borelli

Giovanni Alfonso Borelli (28 January 1608 – 31 December 1679) was an Italian Renaissance mathematician, physicist and physiologist. His work and achievements were far reaching and Borelli's credits includes studying the orbits of the planets and Jupiter's moons, microscopy, examining the constituents of blood and the microscopic movement of the pores of plants.

Perhaps most notably or indeed of most interest to this book, Borelli extended Galileo's rigorous analytical method of testing hypotheses against observation from the world of mechanics into the world of biology. He extensively studied the science of movement in animals or the mechanics of animal locomotion, which is an area of research he began in 1657 and continued until the end of his life. His famous book, which was only published in 1680 after his death, De Motu Animalium (On the Movement of Animals), compares the movement of animals to machines and utilizes mathematics to prove his theories. Amongst his other significant theories and discoveries in relation to movement are:

- Borelli took the suggestion from 17th century anatomists that muscles exhibited a contractile movement and evolved this hypothesis into the conclusion that 'muscles do not exercise vital movement otherwise than by contracting.

- He likened the heart and its action to that of a piston and concluded that arteries have to be elastic.

- Borelli observed that when the body moved forward, so did its centre of gravity, which meant that the swinging of the limbs followed in order to maintain balance.

- Prior to Newton publishing the Laws of Motion, Borelli calculated the forces required for equilibrium in various joints of the human body.

- Borelli was the first to show that levers of the musculoskeletal system, rather than force, magnify motion and determine the body's centre of gravity.

- Borelli suggested that the body could be represented as a system of solids interconnected with 2D or 3D pivotal joints.

For these discoveries amongst others, Borelli is credited

with the title of the father of modern biomechanics, with the American Society of Biomechanics still using the Giovanni Borelli Award as the highest honour for research in the field of biomechanics.

The lever system principle

A lever is one of the six simple machines identified by Renaissance scientists: lever, pulley, inclined plane, wedge, screw, wheel and axle. A lever can be defined as a machine consisting of a beam or rigid rod, pivoted at a fixed hinge or single point fulcrum. A lever amplifies an input force to provide a greater output force, which is said to provide leverage. The ratio of the output force to the input force is the ideal mechanical advantage of the lever and can be utilised to move external objects.

Archimedes is credited with the earliest writings regarding levers, dating back to the 3rd century BC and although he did not invent the lever, he was the first to explain them and apply the correct mathematics to the physical principle of levers.

'Give me a place to stand, and I shall move the Earth with it.'

\- Archimedes

There are three classes of levers, which are classified depending on the relative positions of the fulcrum and the input force; also known as effort, and the output force; also known as load or resistance:

- Class 1: the fulcrum is central and effort is applied one side of the fulcrum, with resistance being applied on the other. The mechanical advantage of a class 1 lever may be more or less than 1. Examples of class 1 levers include a seesaw, a crowbar or a pair of scissors.

- Class 2: the resistance is central and effort is applied one side of the resistance, with the fulcrum located on the other side. The mechanical advantage of a class 2 lever is always greater than 1. Examples of class 2 levers include a wheelbarrow, a car brake pedal or a nutcracker.

- Class 3: the effort is central and the resistance is on one side of the effort, with the fulcrum located on the other side. The mechanical advantage of a class 3 lever is always less than 1. An example of class 3 lever includes a pair of tweezers.

In all classes of levers the lever must be directly in contact with the fulcrum for the lever to be applicable and work as described.

Borelli and the lever system

Borelli's ideas around movement were influenced by Descartes mechanical physiological ideals and he too believed that the human body was a machine, with machine parts making up the whole. Borelli was also inspired by Galileo and his work with animals, who had already concluded that larger animals had relatively thicker bones to support themselves. Borelli also focused on Archimedes six simple machines and specifically worked with the lever principle in relation to movement.

From the scientists who went before him Borelli had a strong overview of mechanics and took the lever principle and applied it to the movement of animals. Borelli concluded that if levers were found in an animal's movement then they could also be used when looking at the movement of a human being. Borelli believed bones to be true levers with the force required to make movement being affected by the length of the limb, the distance to the muscles and the position of the joint. The power or force in and out of a lever must be the same, which means it is always in perfect balance.

He was the first to understand and compare the human body to a machine, composed of several levers, in the firm belief that God created the whole world based on geometrical principles. He stated that the levers of the musculoskeletal system magnify motion rather than force, so that muscles must produce much larger forces than those resisting the motion and that bones serve as levers and muscles function according to mathematical principles; this became a basic principle for modelling human motion. This assumption came from Euclidean geometry of straight lines meeting at a defined angle and provided a postulate that the whole body in its individual parts are connected through a fixed point (the fulcrum), which provides a linear lever system.

Levers are considered one dimensional as they only move in one plane or direction. However, the wheel and axle, which is one of the six simple machines is classified as a rotational lever as these two parts rotate together and transfer force from one part to the other (from wheel to axle or vice versa).

Borelli used the wheel and axel as a lever to represent the articulation between the bone and the joint. This allowed him to explore rotation, which resulted in a perfect symmetrical circle; another of Euclid's geometric shapes. In this configuration a hinge, or bearing, supports the rotation of the axle and provides a rotational lever with loads applied at a given point, known as a tangent, that are balanced around the hinge, which is the fulcrum.

Open chain link system

The current lever system used in biomechanics is also known as the open chain link system, which provides the foundations of kinematics that is widely used in movement science. An open link system is where one part of the chain initiates the action of a second part and so on. This occurs with each part being isolated from the next, so one break in the chain or link will stop the full reaction of the chain. An open chain can be mathematically equated and this is the system that Borelli's utilised in his static mechanics and linear motions. In other words a lever system is an open chain link system with a start and end point. Due to the combination of isolated parts performing in a predictable and linear manner, mathematics can easily equate any variables that a lever system produces.

A closed chain on the other hand, is an integrated and self-organising system. More to come on this in section three; the future...

Borelli as the father of biomechanics

Borelli combined the Cartesian mechanistic framework with Galileo's emphasis on mathematics in his view of the mechanical biological body. Borelli's great work is almost wholly a study of animal statics in an attempt to change from visual (qualitative) observation to quantitative measurements, and was crucial for the emergence of biomechanics.

Borelli suggested that movement represents the real object of mathematics and should be quantified as such through different isolated parts, with the main concern being the forces acting on the body. To represent the forces acting upon the joint in a lever system, Borelli used Euclidian geometry and applied it within static mechanics, which allowed him to analyse the forces acting on the body through a solitary position of freedom. This is an isolated state, within a linear motion, occurring at a single point within the framework of rigid body dynamics. For Borelli to achieve this and measure the forces through the body, he utilised static mechanical forces. Or in other words he took his measurements when the body was stationary and in a single position. This resulted in a model of the body, based on the lever system with a single degree of freedom.

Borelli's significant influence on applying mechanics to human motion has inspired many scientists and contemporary Borelli-inspired models of the human body represent the skeleton as a poly-linker with pin joints in-between solid links. These poly-linker models are the working basis of the Lagrange equations used in today's computerised biomechanical analysis software packages. These calculations work out the tension in muscles, bones and ligaments using the assumption and constraints of solid mechanics.

Borelli's hypothesis, based on the lever principle outlined by Archimedes, is still used in biomechanics today with the model that skeletal muscles act on bones, which are the levers, to lift weights or produce motion. Even in engineering mechanics, the lever principle has evolved to include 6 degrees of freedom as suggested by Euler's work.

So what's the problem?

On closer inspection there appears to be numerous fundamental flaws to the preceding information when looking in context of the human body. The lever principle works just fine with inanimate objects but for a lever to work in the human body, the fulcrum, which in the case of biomechanics is the joint, must be fixed and the bones must be touching. If the bones are touching and the fulcrum or joint is fixed then there would be no movement at all, let alone at the joint. Think about it this way; if bone a) is touching bone b) (with a fixed joint in-between), touching bone c) (with a fixed joint in-between), touching bone d) etc. then there would only be a static model and no movement.

Another major discrepancy is that if levers were in the body the way Borelli defined, with two touching bones then the lever (the bone) must be in direct contact with the fulcrum (the joint), not including any other tissue such as cartilage or ligaments as this would result in deformation and the lever involved would no longer be a rigid body or true lever. There is also no energy transfer in a lever system, as firstly, it is a rigid body and without deformation the energy transfer is zero or negligible and secondly, due to this lack of energy transfer the system always remains in balance. This is something that never occurs in humans.

To maintain the input force matching the output force the only force that can be used to keep balance is a static force. This would need to be applied at given points along the lever and if speed happens to increase due to the motion, like all human movement, there would be increased friction and sheering between the fixed fulcrum (the joint) and the fixed lever (the bone). This in turn would produce heat, which mechanical objects may benefit from but excess heat generated around the joint would prove highly detrimental.

The only time where Borelli's lever principles may be

applicable is in a disease state like arthritis, where bones are touching and there is an increased friction and heat around the joint. The position of the fixed fulcrum would also provide stress points located at the point of contact between the force being applied and the lever itself. This would result in forces not being dissipated throughout the system but instead being focused at a given point. This again may prove beneficial when looking at a machine with isolated parts but it is obvious to see that with the human being, as an integrated whole without the transfer of force being disbanded throughout the body, integrated movement, for example walking, would not occur. It is a logical conclusion that Borelli's levers are not applicable to humans otherwise we would see every human have an arthritic condition at every single joint in the human body.

A large number of biologists and biomechanists teaching, studying and researching human movement in our modern age are firmly committed to a mechanistic understanding of how living things move and exist. Their commitment of attempting to understand the living, based on an understanding of the non-living along with the view that each individual part of the system can be mathematical equated to represent the whole, ultimately results in estimation and guess work based on laws designed for machines or static, inanimate objects. These principles are neatly encapsulated in the machine conception of the organism (MCO), which constitutes the central unifying idea of a mechanistic view of the body, through the explanatory and methodical and reductionist approach to how biomechanics studies living systems.

This mechanistic perspective of the human body with the concept that we are composed of parts, lacking any intrinsic relationship to each other means that the source of the machines activities is not a whole system, but made up of individual parts that do not form a unity with other aspects of the system or influence any other parts.

This provides a cataclysmic problem to everyone involved in the study and attempt to provide evolution to the movement community. The MCO model is so ingrained in the minds of working scientists, that the question "What is the nature of movement and the organism?" is not even entering into educated discussions. It is assumed and taken for granted that the mechanisms and mechanistic views have already answered it; that the organism is a machine and therefore moves like one.

Pit Stop Summary

- Borelli used Archimedes lever system, which is a simple machine originally designed for engineering purposes, and applied the principles along with Euclidian mathematics to the movement in animals.

- A lever is a machine consisting of a rigid beam, pivoted at a fixed point known as a hinge, or fulcrum. In biomechanics the bone is the lever, the joint is the fulcrum and the force is the tissue.

- There is no energy transfer in a lever system and the system is always in balance.

- A lever system is an open chain action.

- A lever system is a rigid body working in a linear and one dimensional way.

- True levers are objects, used by engineers within a mechanical framework for engineering purposes. True levers can be used in two ways:

- Firstly, they can be used by humans to move something, to lift something, to open something etc. Examples include:

seesaw, wheelbarrow, scissors, tweezers and a bottle opener.

- Secondly, they can be used as a component of a mechanistic object such as a car break.

- Any joint with more than one degree of freedom is not a true lever.

- Anything that has connection is not a true lever.

- Anything that can bend is not a true lever.

Thinking Cap

NB: Remember this Thinking Cap section contains straight forward questions. I am not trying to catch you out. As you read the questions just use your common sense to give a spontaneous answer. These are the basics and I am sure you as the reader can think of more questions that highlight the issues we face by continuing to use biomechanics, without opening up alternative movement theory possibilities.

1) Do you think a rigid, linear, open chain lever realistically represents the bones in a human body? Or in other words are our bones rigid?

2) Do you think a fixed fulcrum realistically represents our joints? Or in other words are our joints fixed?

3) Can a lever system ever realistically represent the skeletal system when for the principle to work the lever (bone) must be touching the fulcrum/pivot/another bone?

4) Are our bodies always in constant balance?

5) Our joints are able to rotate and spin; is this ever in a perfect circle?

6) Do our bodies only operate in one degree of freedom at any given joint?

7) How would our bodies operate without energy transfer?

8) Are the bones and joints in the human body working in isolation from each other?

9) Can a system based on static force ever truly measure dynamic motion?

Chapter 5

Are we points and constants?

"If I have seen further than others, it is by standing upon the shoulders of giants".

- Sir Isaac Newton

Sir Isaac Newton's Three Laws of Motion

Sir Isaac Newton (1642 – 1726) is known as one of history's most influential scientists. A physicist and mathematician who played an influential role in the scientific revolution with a long list of scientific accomplishments attributed to him, covering a vast width of subjects. His extensive and impressive works included a shared credit for calculus, establishing the laws of universal gravitation and identifying laws of motion. For the interest and purpose of this book we will explore Newton in relation to the foundations of biomechanics. His book, 'Mathematical Principles of Natural Philosophy' was first published in 1687 and is very significant to the world of biomechanics as it is widely recognised as laying the foundations of classical mechanics.

Classical mechanics is concerned with the set of physical laws describing the motion of bodies under the action of a system of forces. The study of the motion of bodies is an ancient one, making classical mechanics one of the oldest and largest subjects in science, engineering and biomechanics. It is also widely known as 'Newtonian mechanics'. When the laws of classical or Newtonian mechanics are applied to objects, they are idealized as single point masses (matter), in the sense that the size and shape of the rigid object's body are neglected in order to focus on its motion more easily. Neither deformation nor rotation of the body are considered. Through his work with planetary motion and gravity Newton suggested that movement of objects on earth could be described by the same principles as celestial bodies. Newton's views of motion were that all objects were rigid, solid, and impenetrable, with the nature of everything being fixed and based upon mathematical constraints.

Newton's three laws of motion

'Mathematical Principles of Natural Philosophy', outlined Newton's three laws of motion for the first time. These three laws laid the foundation for classical mechanics and described the relationship between a body, the forces acting upon that body and the motion as it responds to these forces. These three laws of motion are:

First law – "Everybody perseveres in its state of rest, or of uniform motion in a straight line, unless it is compelled to change that state by forces impressed thereon".

This first law is also known as the law of inertia and means that objects remain in a constant state of velocity. In biomechanics, the late leg swing phase of gait, just prior to the heel strike is considered to be inertia as the extremity is moving forwards in space, with almost no muscles activated at that point. To deal with this particular inertia, the body balances the movement with an eccentric contraction of the hamstring to slow the leg down and prepare it for heel-strike.

Second law – "The alteration of motion is ever proportional to the motive force impressed; and is made in the direction of the straight line in which that force is impressed".

This second law is also known as the law of force (force = mass x acceleration or F = ma) and means that the net force applied to a body, results in proportional acceleration. In biomechanics, all static and dynamic motions have force. Muscles contract and create force on the body's levers (bones and connective tissues) to create movement or even allow to allow the muscular-skeletal system to remain upright, without collapsing on itself.

Third law – "To every action there is always opposed an equal and opposite reaction: or the mutual actions of two bodies upon each other are always equal, and directed to contrary parts".

This third law is also known as the law of action and reaction. In biomechanics, this law describes how forces always come in pairs and that anytime an object is touching another object they are exerting a force as well as gravity always touching every object. So for example, if you think about ground reaction forces; an individual running on hard ground will incur much higher impact forces than an individual running on soft grass.

Newton's law and the inertial reference frame

In the Newtonian laws, all objects are solid and must touch each other in order to create a change based upon an internal reference frame. Without this touch the laws would not be applicable. A fictitious force is a force that acts on all objects, is inertial and whose motion is described by using a non-inertial frame of reference. A fictitious force does not require any physical interaction between two objects and is accelerating (changing) compared to a non-accelerating frame used in Newtonian mechanics and the Cartesian coordinate system. This non-initial reference frame such as that of a rotational frame is not linear and exists with non-uniform motion, which is constantly changing. The inertial frames are always constant, isolated from its surroundings and non-moving and only valid for the three laws where the references are based upon the fixed stars, without rotating occurring at any time. So if objects are not fixed to a fixed point, are rotating, have non-uniform motion and have forces that are not in the physical sense, Newtonian laws and the Cartesian coordinate system, as used in biomechanics will not apply.

The laws of motion in a non-inertial frames do not take the simple form they do in inertial frames and the laws vary from frame to frame depending on the acceleration. So a way to rectify this is to mathematically and deterministically transform all coordinates to an inertial system, by neglecting and taking out all elements associated with the non-initial frames. This provides a model that fits the predictably, deterministic and artificially constructed values to Newtonian two body ideology

As the Newtonian and Cartesian models use isolated elements it is worth speaking about the problem of isolation. An isolated system does not interact with its local or global environment in any way and is one where amongst other things maintains constant energy within the system. This constant energy is where there is no change or exchange of energy occurring at any time. A system in this state is said to be in equilibrium, which includes inertial frames, as energy does not enter or leave the system. Truly isolated physical systems do not exist in reality as there is always interaction with the local and global environments, otherwise there would be no movement, no life (as this becomes mechanical) and no evolution. The concept of an isolated system serves as an unrealistic model in attempt to approximate real-world situations but it is used as it is easily equated in comparison with what happens in reality.

Gravity - The system of the world

Newton compared the universe to a mechanical clock, a faultless machine that continues to tick along with its gears governed by the laws of physics, making every aspect of the machine predictable and deterministic. Newton came up with a mathematical solution to find the positions of the earth and sun and solved this two body problem by providing mathematical equations to explain the two positions. The reason that the two bodies did not collide, move away or fall from the sky became the gravitational mathematics commonly used today. Gravity is the attraction of two or more particles, irrespective of where they are and can be described as the pulling force of innate rigid bodies, based upon a heliocentric system, or in other words; one where the planets revolve around a fixed sun, in a fixed geometric manner.

Gravity was hypothesised to provide an approximation of a shape and predictability. Any mathematical system has the primary objective of finding a pattern, shape, predictability or symmetry. If you have asymmetrical shapes or irregular patterns then finding a unified constant becomes impossible.

The two body problem vs the three body problem and the birth of calculus

Following the success of solving the two body problem Newton attempted to include the workings of the moon, which is known as the three body problem but these equations have never been formulated, due to the random and unpredictable nature of adding a third entity.

Newton used Euclidian geometry and Descartes coordinate system to solve the two body problem and continued to try to solve the three body problem with the same foundation, using God-given shapes of geometry. However, because all entities are moving independently from each other and the relative perspective is not constant it became impossible to solve. Newton believed that God placed the sun, moon and planets in their positions, as well as being responsible for keeping them there. Geometry and mathematics allowed him to predict the positioning and equate the motion between two points.

This unpredictability of adding more than the predictability of two entities gave birth to random theory, chaos theory etc. This metaphorical third person in a two way conversation meant that Newton's laws could not be applied. So instead Newton evolved and refined his number theory to provide a predictable and deterministic mathematical equation that would provide an approximate pattern, where there was no regular patterns to start with; calculus was born.

In the process of evolving his calculus theory, Newton required a foundation to start his mathematical workings from regarding the three body problem. To get over this issue he manipulated the position of the third body in space to solve the problem, which allowed him to continue using Euclidian geometry as he had done to solve the two body problem. These three positions, graphically still form the basis of a triangular shape with right angles, straight lines and are predictable, deterministic, and linear and very much machine like.

Newton then used a coordinate system in combination with calculus to provide evidence supporting his theories on gravity and motion. It was then assumed that all objects must be in balance and uniform in matter, size, shape, rigidity and density, with every point mass attracting every single other point mass along a predictable line. For this to be achieved any external force, such as friction, is not included in the theory and has no relationship with gravity. To truly verify the laws of gravity you would have to know all parts within the system and know every interaction of all the different forces, in all different directions, at all different points in time.

Newton's law of universal gravity states that every point mass attracts every single other point mass, by a force pointing along the line intersecting both points. The force is proportional to the product of the two masses and inversely proportional to the square of the distance between them. The Newtonian view of the action at a distance principle can be described as the equal change in the properties of one element, changing the properties of a second element, that is independent from any influence of a third element and anything in-between the original two elements.

The question is what occurs if there is a third or more interactions, as well as a fictitious force between any of the interaction? This fictitious force could be things such as electrical, magnetic, waves in the form of vibration or sound as well as properties that deal with frictional forces such as air. How can Newton's three laws be applicable to the human body if the gravitational theory that produces these three laws has been brought into question?

The action at a distance principle makes non-physical interactions highly problematic within the current laws and one which requires further exploration. Newton himself felt that the concept of an inexplicable action at a distance was unsatisfactory and that the concept of one body acting upon another body at a distance, through a vacuum, without any other medium being active in between was incomplete and would need adapting in time. This is something quantum mechanics and Einstein's laws of reality have spoken about and documented. So should we be using Einstein's laws to represent gravity instead of Newton's to understand gravity's influence on the biological system on earth?

Newtonian laws in Biomechanics

Biomechanics teaches Newtonian laws but their application to nature and mankind is problematic. It is relatively straight forward to test these laws in the laboratory setting where all conditions can be modified and manipulated to provide constants, which provide measurements. The question is; are these measurements universally valid?

Under Newtonian laws, all objects in question follow the three laws of motion and the laws of gravity to conform to the principles of a clockwork world. Newtonian laws use information based upon celestial mechanics, with the principles being transferred to earth to create classical mechanics. This system is underpinned with the concept that the world is a machine, with Euclidean shapes and the invention of calculus to make these ideas fit.

In biomechanics Newtonian laws are used in the following ways:

a. The foundation of the subject is based upon Newtonian mechanics.

b. Every biomechanical experiment carried out, for example, force platform data, 3D motion capture analysis are all underpinned and equated using Newtonian mechanics.

c. The two body problem is used to look at point a) to point b) in the body. For example, the hand to the elbow or the elbow to the shoulder. This is a link, lever system.

d. All biomechanical equations are based on Newtonian mechanics, with modern computational software using Newtonian mathematics to analyse and replicate human motion.

e. Biomechanics attempts to represent biological systems by using the methods of engineering mechanics.

All of Newton's laws are applied to objects, which are idealized as single point masses (matter). The size and shape of the object's body are neglected in order to focus more easily on its motion along with the deformation, rotation, friction and air resistance. In this way, even a planet can be idealized as a particle for the purpose of analysing its orbital motion around a star. The random inconstant chaos brought about by ever changing environments are of no importance.

Theology and biomechanics

In modern biomechanics the laws and mathematics, which are universally used in all of the underlying theories and hypothesis were established by Sir Isaac Newton. Newton used the ideologies of the geometrical language outlined by Euclid and the positional coordinates of Descartes to provide evidence to his laws of motion, which evolved out of the underlying belief that the world was regular, symmetrical and based on the predictability of regular geometric patterns being found in a predictable space.

It is important to remember that geometry, levers and the laws of motion were all developed in a time where religious views overpowered the scientific climate. There was a strong belief in the external creator in the form of God who was believed to have designed the mechanical order of nature.

If Gods design gave birth to Euclidian geometry, which in turn gave birth to the lever system in the body and Newton's law of motion, which are all strongly imbedded in the mechanistic views underlying the practice of biomechanics today; then religion is at the roots of biomechanics. I am a scientist and an expert in human movement. Using a system of movement analysis based heavily on theological ideas is not an acceptable notion for me in the twenty first century. Of course, it is easy to forget the roots but essentially they are there, deeply imbedded. I consider myself to be an agnostic rather than an atheist and am completely open to a pluralistic, free thinking and open minded world but I prefer not to have my movement science tangled up with religious foundations. But maybe that's just me.

So what's the problem?

Newton's laws are applicable to inanimate objects. However, when we take them out of that environment and apply them to real life and moving, animate beings we start to hit problems. I will discuss the problems encountered with the three laws of motions in accordance with biomechanics firstly, before taking a look at the bigger picture:

First law – "Everybody perseveres in its state of rest, or of uniform motion in a straight line, unless it is compelled to change that state by forces impressed thereon".

The first law implies that the net force and net torque (also known as moment of force) on every part of the system is zero to begin with. The net force equalling zero is known as the first condition for equilibrium. All Newtonian laws are based on a concept of the conservation of energy and apply to isolated, physical systems without any external exchange – neither matter nor energy can enter or exit, but can only move around inside. This can be contrasted with a closed system, which can exchange energy with its surroundings but not matter; and with an open system, which can exchange both matter and energy.

Truly isolated systems cannot exist in nature, other than allegedly the universe itself, and they are thus only hypothetical concepts. The concept of an isolated system can serve as a useful model approximating many real-world situations but this is only a guess. It is an acceptable idealization used in constructing mathematical models. The first law of motion is viewed from an inertial reference frame based on Euclidean geometry and the coordinate system. The object is at rest or in motion with no internal force occurring and no variation or variability within its motion. Any change within an isolated system relies on an external force, which requires that all forces involved within this first law are of the same magnitude, speed and direction. Within this first law of inertia, velocity is a vector of both speed and direction; thus there is constant velocity, constant speed and constant direction making direction and speed predictable and deterministic. It is also key to remember that these laws are based upon two point particles only and in truth there are millions if not billions integrated in all motions and that friction of any kind is neglected from the mathematics in any of these three laws.

Second law – "The alteration of motion is ever proportional to the motive force impressed; and is made in the direction of the straight line in which that force is impressed".

The second law of motion states that the net force on a single object is equal to the rate of change (of its linear momentum in an inertial fixed reference frame). The second law can also be stated in terms of an object's acceleration. Since Newton's second law is only valid for constant-mass systems this has to be an isolated system with its total energy and mass staying constant. This is never the case in nature and the human body. Let's imagine a boundary defining our imagined system, enclosing the two point particles used in Newtonian laws. What is the external force acting on this system? Zero.

We stated in the condition of the problem that no other forces act on any part of the system. Therefore, Newton's second law applied to the entire system tells us that the system's centre of mass cannot be accelerating because within areas of the system there are many centres of mass and therefore much variability occurring at different times. In particle terms, Newton's second law is like the first and only works on the action of two particles being identical in motion and design. By applying Newton's second law it would suggest that a system's centre of mass is not accelerating as all things are equal, which questions the reality of the law in relation to human movement.

Third law – "To every action there is always opposed an equal and opposite reaction: or the mutual actions of two bodies upon each other are always equal, and directed to contrary parts".

The third law of motion states that all forces exist in pairs, with nothing able to occur if more than two interactions are present. This relates directly to the second law and if the second law is violated the third follows. If object a) exerts an equal force and opposite force on a second object, object b), then b) simultaneously exerts an equal and opposite force on a). To satisfy the third law of mutual forces, the interactions can only occur between two rigid bodies, objects with the same design, shape, symmetry, size and substance. A few key things are not taken into account by the third law:

1) Unidirectional force is not taken into consideration in the third law (force is considered linear).

2) Only one kind force is considered, so it is not possible to examine more than two different kinds of forces acting on the two bodies.

3) Force changing over a distance is not taken into consideration. What would occur then if object a) exerts a force on a very distant object b) and it takes time for that force to travel the distance? Whilst traveling it changes its energy (e.g. gravitational force, electrical force or magnetic force) along the way due to the body changing from its initial force. So if object a) moves, say nearer to b), b) may be affected by its change by another force, say c) which was not the original force that was attracting object a). This change of design will also change the pathway that the object a) is taking. With the random and chaotic configurations of the design of the object and the unidirectional force it produces upon the approach of the object, the contact of objects making equal and opposite reactions improbable.

Also consider the possibility that there might exist two unusual particles, with the remarkable property that particle a) is attracted to particle b) and particle b) is repelled by particle a). This is not a mutual force as needed to satisfy this law. Together both forces a) and b) would form a system that continuously accelerates in any direction, particle a) always chasing particle b) (remember what would happen if we added more than two particles and one force?) When two bodies with mass collide, there is, during the collision, an action-reaction pair of contact forces that is repulsive. But the forces in this law are two bodies, which are symmetrical, rigid and of equal size, shape and substance and move in a linear way. Here's where we realize we are in serious trouble as in the real world Newton's laws do not apply to the human body. This is a point students often "know" but they may fail to appreciate its far-reaching implications.

The issue of gravity

There is an anomaly in gravity, which is termed effective gravity. A gravity anomaly is the difference between the observed acceptation of the 9.81m/s predicted value. A positive anomaly has more gravity where as a negative anomaly has lower gravity. It is the difference between the positive and negative anomalies that effects the deviation from the 9.81 model. Friction and air resistance become a contribution to the difference found in the positive and negative anomalies, which shows that this constant model outlined by Newton is not always constant. The second major anomaly of gravity is the omittance of the effects of air resistance and friction in any calculations. So even with these two outliers the model outlined by Newton is not 100% correct and needs investigation when attempting to use it in biomechanics.

The gravitational number, used by Newton (9.81) as a foundation for his three laws of motion has different variations due to the inconstancies with measurement devices used at the time, the various mathematics, different times of day, different locations and even the planets that were used as reference points. For example, the heliocentric theory of the earth circulating around the sun, which is what Newton used for his gravitational laws, is today being questioned with a different opinion of a helical shape being theorised. This is where the sun creates a vortex around the planets. If this were the case then gravity theory may change.

Newton's law of gravity did not explain how one thing could act on another instantly, across any distance, without anything being in-between them; empty space without energy. However, whenever objects attract other objects, vibrations in a bioelectrical field are induced (e.g. sound waves, electrical currents) resulting in the empty space now containing energy. It is also impossible to measure every atom and every star, so the gravitational law is a hypothesis. Newton himself recognised the fact that there were problems with the theory and as there were no mathematics to back up his hypothesis he invented a whole new branch of mathematics, called fluxions, to justify his theory. This later became calculus, which includes elements within the equations based upon gravitational information that had never actually been observed.

Pit Stop Summary

- Newton adapted the principles of celestial mechanics to create classical mechanics, which is also known as Newtonian mechanics.

- Newton's 3 laws of motion can be summarised as the law of inertia, the law of force and the law of action and reaction.

- Newton invented calculus whilst trying to solve the two body problem and specifically the mathematical solution to find the positions of the earth and sun.

- Newton was the first scientist to recognise the influence of gravity and provided it as the reason for two bodies not colliding, moving away from each other or falling from the sky.

- Newton found it impossible to solve the three body problem, as all entities are moving independently from each other and the relative perspective is not constant. Newton instead developed calculus to provide a predictable, deterministic mathematical equation to provide an approximation of pattern, when there was none to start with.

- Every experiment in modern biomechanics is equated based on the principles of Newtonian mechanics.

Thinking Cap

NB: Remember this Thinking Cap section contains straight forward questions. I am not trying to catch you out. As you read the questions just use your common sense to give a spontaneous answer. These are the basics and I am sure you as the reader can think of more questions that highlight the issues we face by continuing to use biomechanics, without opening up alternative movement theory possibilities.

1. What happens if more than one particle acting upon one object is being observed at the same time?

2. What happens if friction and air resistance are taken into consideration with gravity? Does this affect the 9.81 constant number that is current used?

3. What happens if the line of force was not straight?

4. What happens if nature is not symmetrical?

5. Is everything truly equal?

6. Are we isolated from everything?

7. What happens if everything can deform and is not purely rigid?

8. Are we single point particles?

9. Are there no internal forces?

10. If Newton's mathematics was only applicable for a two body problem how can we accept this mathematics to be accurate for a three body problem or more?

Part 2. The Present

Human biomechanics: the current theory of human movement.

Chapter 6

What is human biomechanics?

"The area of science concerned with the analysis of mechanics of human movement. In other words it is the science of explaining how and why the human body moves in the way that it does".

- The British Association of Sport and Exercise Sciences

Biomechanics looks at forces acting on the human body. The subject is considered to be closely related to engineering as traditional engineering sciences are utilised to analyse biological systems. As we have discovered in the first part of this book, biomechanics draws on the work of some of history's great scientists:

- Euclid provided Euclidian geometry, which biomechanical modelling still uses today.

- Rene Descartes provided the Cartesian coordinate system, which modern biomechanics uses to pinpoint a point of reference (such as a bone or joint) in a three dimensional model.

- Giovanni Alfonso Borelli brought the study of mechanics into the study of motion and provided the adaptation of the lever system into the human body.

- Sir Isaac Newton defined the laws of motion and gravity. Newtonian mechanics provides a framework for approximations of mechanics applied to the human body and Newton's calculations are still used today in modern biomechanics.

Biomechanics is sometimes described as the physics of movement. Mechanics describes the laws of motion and biomechanics uses these same laws of motion but in reference to the biological system. It is the area of scientific study that applies the laws of mechanics to human movement and performance, to understand the mechanical cause-effect relationship of human movement. It looks quantitatively at human movement, using mathematical modelling, measurements and computer simulation to analyse and gain understanding of performance. The field of biomechanics uses biomechanical analysis to study how human beings move and helps us to:

- Describe human movement.

- Explain human movement.

- Predict human movement.

- Predict mechanical outcome of sport.

- Define and understand movement skills.

- Refine the coaching process.

- Advise on minimising and preventing injury.

- Equipment design and usage.

- Prosthetics design.

Inverse dynamics

The subsection of inverse dynamics in relation to biomechanics is known as inverse rigid-body dynamics, which is a method used to compute forces and/or torques (moments of force) based on the motion of a body. The term inverse dynamics is used as forward dynamics equations of motion are reversed to derive joint moments.

The limbs of the human body are represented as a link system, which can be broken down into various parts. Inverse dynamics uses certain set assumptions and Newtonian mechanics to calculate the net turning effect of a joint (including the muscles and ligaments) necessary to produce the motion seen in the joint. The moments of force are then used to calculate the mechanical work performed by that moment of force. Biomechanists can use joint moments to work out muscle forces and estimate muscle activation from kinematic motion.

Joint moments (force) can only be calculated at each joint

if:

1. The joints are frictionless pin-joints.

2. The segments are rigid with mass concentrated at their centres of mass.

3. There is no co-contraction of agonist and antagonist muscles.

4. That air friction is minimal.

5. The equations of motion necessary for these computations are based on Newtonian mechanics

Biomechanics uses inverse dynamics to look at and analyse human movement. Real human movement is looked at and represented as a stick or link man, which is then broken down into a free body diagram to understand isolated movement. The information taken from the link or stick man representation and free body diagram analysis provides biomechanists with data to help achieve their objectives of analysis.

Inverse dynamics in relation to biomechanical model:

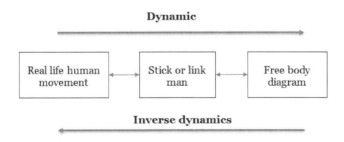

Figure 2

The theory is not the practice – a note on functional biomechanics

Functional biomechanics is seen as the benchmark of respectability in the functional movement world. This area of research is largely credited to Gary Gray, who is an American physio therapist responsible for evolving physiotherapy treatment from a static position, on a couch to a more dynamic, real-life position. From Gray's ground breaking work many variations and systems have sprung but he is considered as the forefather of applied biomechanics.

Gray's work has evolved the biomechanical theory of three degrees of freedom to a more advanced model of six degrees of angulation, where each joint and global movement as a whole can move:

- forward and backwards

- side to side

- left and right

Practically the efficacy of functional biomechanics is highly acclaimed and areas of research into functional biomechanics has made huge breakthroughs in the practical arena. However, there is the same issue of attempting to fit advanced practical work into outdated scientific theory. To scientifically justify the application of the work being carried out, practitioners still have to use biomechanical ideas to justify their belief system. Unfortunately, this means that many advanced movement practitioners with ground breaking techniques and high rates of professional efficacy are failing to gain scientific acceptance, acknowledgement and even recognition.

So we are in the situation as movement practitioners, where we have far more advanced practical methods available to us than ever before. And let's face it; this is where it really counts. But often applied methods work practically in one way and then there is an attempt to use the old paradigm of movement scientific theory to justify their working. Although these methods may get results, have high efficacy and be highly respected within the practical arena, it is currently impossible to justify them with the current biomechanical thinking, resulting in a chasm between this practical work and the acceptance of science.

Does biomechanics ever have a place?

You are probably thinking by now that for a biomechanist I have an obvious dislike for the subject area. However, that is not completely true. My real passion and respect is for human movement and unfortunately, I feel that biomechanics as a subject area does not do human movement justice from a theoretical standpoint. I strongly believe that we are ready to take the theory of human movement to a more elevated understanding than the current universally accepted perspective. However, biomechanics as the subject stands does come into its own in certain areas. Biomechanics, as a research and subject area is still completely valid for contributing towards:

- Equipment design

- Prosthetic design

- Ergonomics

The reason behind this is that the above areas are all mechanically engineered, whereas the human body is not. I therefore believe that biomechanics as an existing model comes into its own in the areas of study that involve artificial, inanimate objects due to the engineering aspect.

Pit Stop Summary

- Biomechanics is the analysis of human movement with the aim of understanding how and why we move as human beings.

- Biomechanics draws on the work of many great scientists. However, the study of biomechanics is primarily founded on mechanical laws, designed for innate objects.

- Biomechanics primarily looks quantitatively at human movement, using mathematical modelling, measurements and computer analysis.

- Functional biomechanics (and many applied movement therapies) have evolved to a far higher level and understanding than the current scientific model and theory of human movement.

- Biomechanics, in its current form, is still valid for equipment, prosthetic and ergonomics due to the engineering aspect.

Thinking Cap

NB: Remember this Thinking Cap section contains straight forward questions. I am not trying to catch you out. As you read the questions just use your common sense to give a spontaneous answer. These are the basics and I am sure you as the reader can think of more questions that highlight the issues we face by continuing to use biomechanics, without opening up alternative movement theory possibilities.

1) Can any law designed, analysed and implemented on inanimate objects represent living structures in any way?

2) Can one dimension Euclidean shapes represent the living structures in any way?

3) Is the lever system how we move?

4) Can we be represented by a fixed point in a fixed reference frame?

5) Can we use predictions in one direction to represent what occurs at different times?

Chapter 7

The biomechanists tool kit

"We become what we behold. We shape our tools, and thereafter our tools shape us."

- Marshall McLuhan

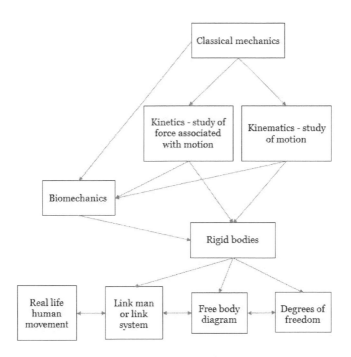

Figure 3

Biomechanics, uses principles directly from classical mechanics as well as the sub divisions of kinetics and kinematics. Kinetics, kinematics and biomechanics all use the principle of rigid bodies at their foundation.

Kinematics and kinetics

Kinematics is the branch of classical mechanics that describes the study of motion and is sometimes referred to as the geometry of motion. Kinematics describes the motion of points, objects and systems of objects without considering the cause of motion and is thought of as a qualitative understanding of motion. To describe motion, kinematics studies the trajectories of points, lines and other geometric objects and their differential properties such as velocity and acceleration. This is represented by an object within the coordinate system, using a Euclidean geometric reference frame.

Kinetics is the study of the forces associated with motion and looks at the external forces that can produce a change of motion on an object. It is an area of study based directly on Newtonian laws and is considered the quantitative understanding of motion.

Two, four and six bar link systems

Newton's system was a two-bar theory by default of the linear calculus used. This means that the mathematics takes into account the calculation from point a) to point b) and point b) to point c). Therefore to make the mathematics viable, this two-bar system is still used in biomechanics today

There have been some studies that have used a four-bar system, which have looked at using the tissue of the body in addition to just the bones that are considered in a two-bar system. This more complex, four-bar model incorporates bone and tissue, with studies having looked at ligaments in the knee and the jaw position of fish by linking two, two-bar systems together. However, even by using the four-bar system, which at this point is still not widely accepted in biomechanical circles, this theory must still use all the same principles and theories both practically and mathematically as the two-bar system, as it is essentially two, two-bar systems joined together.

A two-bar link, is an isolated entity originating from Borelli's principles, which is only concerned with connecting the two links together, independent from its surrounding environment. There is no encasement of the two links within any biological structure and is therefore an ideology without an end point. The four-bar linkage, also called a four-bar is a model of the simplest movable closed chain linkage. This means that the links are connected via biological tissue and consists of four links, which can be bones or soft tissue. Generally, the joints are configured so the links move in parallel planes, and the assembly is called a planar four-bar linkage. If the linkage has four hinged joints with axes angled to intersect in a single point, then the links move on concentric spheres and the assembly is called a spherical four-bar linkage. Planar four-bar linkages are constructed from four links connected in a loop by four one degree of freedom joints. A joint may be either a revolute (hinge and pin joint) or a sliding joint.

To satisfy a four-bar link system, one link is usually fixed, which is called the ground link, fixed link or the frame. The two links connected to the frame are called the grounded links and are generally the input and output links of the system, sometimes called the input link and output link. The last link is the floating link, which is also called a coupler or connecting rod because it connects an input to the output.

There have been attempts of people using a six-bar linkage or six bar to represent the human body but this just follows the same ideology as the two and four bar systems. The only difference between the two and four or six bar is that the four or six bar links move in parallel planes, which has been suggested that the loop of a four or six-bar may incorporate the musculoskeletal system, whereas the conventional tow-bar model utilised by biomechanics only serves to represent the skeletal system.

A six-bar linkage is a mechanism constructed from six links and seven joints. Each joint of a linkage connects two links, and a binary link supports two joints. If we consider a hexagon to be constructed from six binary links, with six of the seven joints forming its vertical points, then the seventh joint can be added to connect two sides of the hexagon to form a six-bar linkage, with two ternary links connected by one joint. A six-bar linkage can also be constructed by first assembling five binary links into a pentagon, which uses five of the seven joints, and then completing the linkage by adding a binary link that connects two sides of the pentagon. This again creates two ternary links (one part with three joints, like a triangle) that are now separated by one or more binary links.

By evolving this model from a two bar to a four bar and from a four bar to a six bar, more links and bars are added to the chain providing more scope for the positions to change shape. However, whether the model being used is a two, four or six bar link system it will still only have predominantly one degree of freedom at most joints. So regardless of whether a two, four or six bar model is used it will still be: rigid; remain based upon the design of a Euclidean shape of a triangle, square, hexagon or straight line; have no internal power source and must only work from external forces. Also, for a four and six bar link system to work, there must always be one fixed link to maintain the integrity of the chain

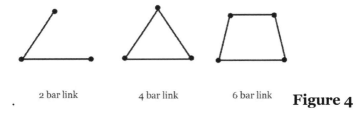

2 bar link   4 bar link   6 bar link   **Figure 4**

So to clarify. Biomechanics currently uses a 2-bar link system. 4-bar link systems have been examined in relation to the knee and the knee ligaments but this model is still not common knowledge in mainstream biomechanical circles. 6-bar link systems are mainly used in engineering but there are a handful of practitioners trying to fit the 6-bar link system into the human body. Still with all the aforementioned attributes. Does adding an extra bar or two make this model any more realistic and representative of human movement?

Kinematic chains

Biomechanics uses a kinematic chain to represent the organism based on geometrical shapes of a straight lined, two-bar (e.g. a bone) or a rectangular four-bar (e.g. the trunk). The kinematic chain is either a serial chain meaning links are added together, which is used for analysis of isolated limbs or a branched chain, which represents larger sections of the body or the whole body as a series of serial chains. The kinematic chain is examined in isolation to the whole system and the majority of joints are considered to have one degree of freedom such as a hinge, revolute or pivot joints.

The chain is rigid in nature and uses two-bar mathematics, which is predictable and constant within a static environment. The simplest form of kinematic chains that are used in biomechanics is a kinematic pair, which is a connection between two or more links.

A kinematic pair is easy to mathematical equate and favoured in biomechanics as it follows the two-bar link system that was used by Benedetti and Borelli. However, although it is compatible in theory the application differs widely. These ideas aim to represent the musculoskeletal system but do it through the use of static analysis.

If the body was a two-bar link as spoken about by Benedetti and Borelli each joint must be stabilized or mobilized by local forces. Muscles that span the individual joint, would only be able to initiate movement using external forces like gravity. With tissues, such as ligaments only playing a supporting role by stabilizing the joint, without playing any active part in the movement itself. This is due to energy being perfectly balanced in a lever system and to change this balance an external force is needed to start the reaction. Once started forces are being produced and transmit little power throughout the structure due to the locality of forces involved in a two bar link system and once the external force is reduced so are the internal forces.

Two or more rigid bodies in space are collectively called a rigid body system and move independently from each other via rigid transformations, which hinder the motion of these independent rigid bodies with kinematic constraints. Kinematic constraints are constraints between rigid bodies that result in the decrease of the degrees of freedom of the rigid body system to just one. The constraint equations of a kinematic chain devised from algebraic equations are used to equate the movement and degrees of freedom possible at each joint, in relation to the geometric shape of the links in the chain. In a traditional kinematic chain, if one part of the chain fails all the chain will fail because of it being a series of isolated parts. This does not occur in any biological structure as they work as a whole, rather than in an isolated chain or series of parts.

The stick man or link man

Biomechanics builds up the isolated segments (dots) created from producing a free body diagram (FBD), which are linked together to create a link or stick man illustration, which is based on Borelli's lever system. And vice versa, a link or stick man illustration can be broken down to isolated parts or a free body diagram (FBD). Usually, biomechanical software packages work by taking camera analysis of the individual carrying out the activity within a three dimensional system and then computerise the individual to become a stick man on screen. Biomechanics uses mathematical equations, computer graphic representations and the estimated forces, movements and reactions that occur in isolated parts of the body. All of these parts are then put back together to represent the human body. The isolated parts are put back together by linking part a) to b), b) to c) and so on in a link man, lever system format, which can be used for coaching or analysis purposes. These representations are also used to predict movement that is likely to occur. However, it must be remembered that the data collected is free from acceleration or velocity with predications being in a steady state. In other words these predictions are carried out without taking acceleration or change of speed into account.

A link man representation is a two-bar model and can be shown as an isolated limb or a series of two-bar links, joined together to create a whole representation of the human body. To put this in perspective regarding the body, a two-bar link can be the arm (finger to the elbow and elbow to the shoulder) and the legs (toe to the knee and knee to the hip). These two-bar serial kinematic chains are linked together to form binary chains, which are three or more links together. For example, the binary link from the hand to the shoulder are:

Shoulder bone	Shoulder joint	Upper arm bone	Elbow joint	Forearm bone	Wrist joint	Hand
Link	Joint	Link	Joint	Link	Joint	Link

Forget the spine

Figure 5 shows how by adding another bar to the branched kinematic chain the model moves from a two bar, to a three bar, to a four bar link system. A four bar link is termed a quaternary link, which means one body has four connections to the trunk (a square or hexagon).

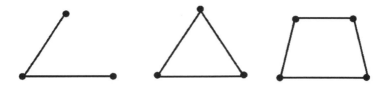

Figure 5

For example, the trunk with four attachments in a human body can be the torso with four attachments for four limbs (two arms and two legs). So this means when biomechanics uses a free body diagram for the trunk it does not use the spine in its representation and has four joints in total. Usually, there are two dots and one link/bar representing the whole spine if a two bar system is used. So the top dot might represent the bottom of the skull and the bottom dot the bottom of the spine. There is no consideration for the rest of the spine. If a four bar system is used to represent the trunk, then the spine is not represented at all.

Free body diagram – pieces of the puzzle

A free body diagram (FBD), also sometimes called a force diagram, is a pictorial device, often a rough working sketch, used by engineers and physicists to analyse the forces and moments acting on a rigid body based upon the lever system. A free body diagram (FBD) is a graphical representation of an isolated body segment, or several linked body segments, which show the application, direction and magnitude of forces acting on the segment. FBD's use the mechanistic viewpoint that the body is designed as a single entity or as an object of several link connected bodies that are isolated and separate from other surrounding body segments.

The free body diagram (FBD) is a major cornerstone of biomechanical analysis as it shows applied forces and moments and aims to calculate reactions of segments of the body and therefore predict movement. Often a FBD does not show the entire physical body but rather just a portion of it. A FBD consists of:

- Dots – representing a simplified version of the body.

- Arrows – representing forces pointing in the directing they act on the body.

- Curved arrows – representing moments, pointing in the direction they act on the body.

- A box – representing the coordinate system, showing the area that the movement happens in and to provide a reference frame for calculations.

The description of 'free' in the term free body diagram (FBD) means that each section of the body being represented is isolated (or free from) any other section of the body. A FBD is free in the following ways:

- Free from constraints.

- Free from any other body segment (isolated from other body parts).

- Free from forces exerted *by* the free body (only forces acting *on* the free body are considered as if the forces acting on the free body and exerted by the free body where both shown then they would cancel out).

- Free from internal forces exerted by one part of the free body on another part.

- Free from acceleration or velocity.

So how are free body diagrams actually used in biomechanics?

FBD's are very commonly used in biomechanics. An example is where the FBD is used in order to determine the forces and torques on the ankle, knee, and hip joints of the lower limb (foot, leg, and thigh) during locomotion. But the FBD can be applied to any problem where the laws of mechanics are needed to solve a problem by the use of inverse dynamics.

To use a free body diagram you must decide which body segment (or segments) is (are) to be isolated from all surrounding bodies and make sure you understand where the separation points are, this is because these models represent the limb segments as rigid levers joined by hinge joints. The FBD is only applicable if only one body/object is involved and that singular body is in isolation.

Therefore a FBD can only work if the body segment is isolated from other body parts and can only take in force rather than exert force. This model is obviously lacking significant points in comparison with real human form and human movement. Nothing in human movement can be considered in isolation. Human movement is chaotic, complex and based on a web of interactions of subsystems, both within the human body as well as the external environment.

The problem of course for biomechanists, is that human movement is too complicated. The forces and mathematics will only work if reality is simplified, so the body is broken down into a bunch of dots that represent single points. For example, the arm will be broken down into isolated and independent parts. Once this has been done and the human form has been reduced to dots then the forces, movements and reactions at each of these isolated parts can be estimated.

So essentially, for a biomechanist to find out what forces are acting on the body, to analyse movement and also predict the reactions that will occur due to these forces and movement, a FBD is used to reduce the complexity of movement and allow mathematics to be applied. The FBD is drawn out as an estimation on paper or more commonly in modern biomechanics on a computer package. Then Newtonian laws of physics are used to find a number that represents the force, movement or reaction.

Usually a biomechanist will also want to understand how an individual part moves through space. So the isolated part, the forces, movement and reaction all need to be placed in a system, where the body parts position can be charted in space. The box used to confine the movement to provide a representation of the isolated part is positioned is the Descartes coordinate system. So the isolated body part is positioned somewhere within a boxed reference frame to analyse the different positions, forces, movement and reactions according to Euclidean geometry and then equated via Newtonian mechanics.

So what's the problem?

In total a free body diagram uses seventeen sections to represent the entire body, using lever terminology and teachings. Separate bones and joints are not considered at all for the spine, hands, feet and head. So a FBD completely omits the seventy two joints in the spine and pelvis, sixty six in the feet and fifty eight in the hands, not to mention the skull. In total biomechanics does not consider the use of over one hundred and ninety six joints. So you can imagine how many degrees of freedom it is failing to take into account.

The following is an example of a sequence followed in biomechanics, utilizing a FBD, when a question needs answering about human movement:

1. You select the part of the system to be studied.

2. Hypothesise the characteristics of the system, which usually involves simplifying the system even further, into parts.

3. Construct a conceptual model by applying the principles of mechanics to this simplified and idealised part.

4. Study the consequences.

5. Compare this to past information and predict the rest of the behaviour of the system.

6. If this meets with approval and acceptance through the use of a statistical set of equations then the information is used. If not, the above process starts over to find what is needed for acceptance by making different assumptions.

So for biomechanics to gain approval and acceptance from universities, for research purposes, government backed projects, as well as serving the community in a sporting, rehabilitative or recreational way, the human organism is reduced to a simplistic model of parts that represents the whole. By reducing the organism down to its bare essentials a basis is established, not only for understanding how things work but also for predicting how they will behave in a quantifiable fashion. By applying the theories of classical mechanics approximations are made to the mechanics of many biological systems. This is then justified by obtaining a number from a man-made statistical system, which is based upon the representation of a machine. This is not a true representation of human movement; this is engineering!

Pit Stop Summary

- Biomechanics is based on the principle of rigid bodies.

- Kinematics describes the study of motion, whereas kinetics studies the forces associated with motion.

- Biomechanics uses kinematic chains to represent the human body, also known as a link or stick man, based upon the lever, two bar-link system.

- Kinematic chains, from a traditional biomechanical standpoint have only one degree of freedom.

- Biomechanics uses free body diagrams (a model built up of dots), linked together to create a link or stick man, which is a series of two-bar links, joined together.

- The FBD and link man models look at the human body in isolation, reducing the human body down to a simplified version where mathematics can be applied.

- A FBD and link man does not take into account internal forces, only external forces, which means this model is not compatible with living, moving beings as internal forces generate motion.

Thinking Cap

NB: Remember this Thinking Cap section contains straight forward questions. I am not trying to catch you out. As you read the questions just use your common sense to give a spontaneous answer. These are the basics and I am sure you as the reader can think of more questions that highlight the issues we face by continuing to use biomechanics, without opening up alternative movement theory possibilities.

1. Kinematic chains are based on rigid bodies. Is the human body rigid?

2. Are we made of frictionless hinge and pin joints, with just one degree of freedom?

3. Can our bodies be compared to a mathematical model based upon Euclidean geometry, made up of lines, triangles, circles and squares?

4. The kinematic chain has one degree of freedom. Do we move in one direction only?

5. A kinematic chain has a fixed part to the chain; is there a fixed point in nature and mankind?

6. Do we have isolated parts?

7.   Do our forces only travel a small distance? With no internal forces occurring?

8.   Can we only transfer force directly to the next isolated part?

9.   Is nature and mankind only able to move in a linear direction?

10. Do we only have one degree of freedom available to us? Or do you think nature and mankind are single dimensional forms?

11. Are all bodies a free body? Or in other words in isolation?

12. Can there be only one body/object/involved in all actions?

13. How can there be no force given out by the free body?

14. How can there be no internal force within the body?

15. Is it possible to find a mathematical model that best fits the answer we already want to find?

16. Is it possible to predict movement in the rest of the body, based on examining an isolated part of it?

Chapter 8

Degrees of freedom. How free is free?

"There are considerable advantages to using many degrees of freedom to store information, stability and controllability being perhaps the most important".

- Seth Lloyd

A degree of freedom of a physical system is an independent parameter that is necessary to characterize the state of a physical system in space, with the body being represented as a rigid body around revolute joints in order to simplify the mathematical analysis. It will achieve this by using the three dimensional coordinate system where a single particle in space requires three coordinates so it has three degrees of freedom. The number of input coordinates is also termed the mobility of the linkage system. It is bound via the geometric constraints of the lever system and is formed as a two, four or six bar link system.

An object in free space, according to engineering principles has six degrees of freedom (DOF), whereas a fixed object has zero degrees of freedom. The six degrees of freedom (6DOF) represent the freedom of movement associated with a rigid body in a three-dimensional space. The six degrees of freedom (6DOF) can be separated into two categories:

Perpendicular degrees of freedom -

1.   Heave (up/down)

2.   Surge (forward/backward)

3.   Sway (moving left/right)

Rotational degrees of freedom –

4.   Pitch (leaning forward/backward)

5.   Yaw (turning left/right)

6.   Roll (tilting side to side)

Biomechanics only uses three axis to enable the movements being described to fit into the Cartesian coordinate system, whereas engineering uses six. The three degrees of freedom (3DOF) accounted for in biomechanics are:

	Degrees of freedom	Movement	Anatomical term	Cartesian axis
1	Surge	Forward/backward	Sagittal plane	X axis
2	Sway	Moving left/right	Frontal plane	Y axis

3	Yaw	Turning left/right	Transverse plane	Z axis

Table 2 - The three degrees of freedom in biomechanics

These 3DOF are classified in movement terms as sagittal, frontal and transverse and describe global or gross movements; meaning they are descriptions for the whole body moving through space. Even by only using 3DOF to describe movement, it would suggest that these should be applicable to each joint within the link system. However, the only two joints in the body that biomechanics states has 3DOF is at the hip and shoulder. All of the other joints are considered to have one or two degrees of freedom and the degrees of freedom of bones and soft tissue is not taken into consideration at all.

The human body is made up of around two hundred and thirty joints. Because Borelli's lever system was built on 1DOF, which is known as a revolute joint, biomechanics for the sake of mathematics predominantly uses 1DOF. Therefore, by adding up the DOF for every movable and semi-movable joint in the human body, biomechanics calculates that the human body has 230 - 244 DOF. The interesting thing is that a free body diagram considers only seventeen main sections of the body with no separation of the spine, hands or feet and rather than most joints being considered to have multiple DOF, biomechanics describes most joints as having only 1DOF.

This means that although engineering uses 6DOF, the analysis of our movement in biomechanics is reduced down to 3DOF as a gross motor unit and mainly 1 or 2DOF in its joint motion. For example, the shoulder is considered to have 3DOF, whereas the knee or the elbow are considered to only have 1DOF. So ultimately engineering is using a more complex model to talk about the movement of static structure than biomechanics is using to describe, analyse and predict the movement of the human body.

Interestingly, from an engineering perspective when looking at robots and DOF, the actual exact number of moving parts are not included as the number would not be quantifiable. If robots create a problem for engineers, when taken in context of 6DOF then imagine how much simpler the analysis of human movement has to be, using only 3DOF.

Range of motion

If the term 'degrees of freedom' sounds a little familiar, it is because it is also the term commonly used to describe the range of motion that a joint has. This information on degrees of freedom, has obvious implications for biomechanical understanding but also for the movement rehabilitation environment where range of motion is commonly used as a diagnostic tool and to assist with rehabilitative programmes.

The range of motion (ROM), is the distance that a movable object may normally travel while properly attached to another. It is also called range of travel, particularly when talking about mechanical devices. Each specific joint has a normal range of motion that is expressed in degrees. The devices to measure range of motion in the joints of the body include the goniometer and inclinometer, which use a stationary arm, protractor, fulcrum, and movement arm to measure the angle from the axis of the joint. To find these measurements it must be assumed that the body is modelled as a lever system in a kinematic chain, with small amounts of movement based in a static environment. Biomechanics uses reference points for range of motion, depending on certain variables, such as age, sex, height, dimensions of limbs etc., which are taken from biomechanical anthropometry.

Pit Stop Summary

- Engineering uses 6DOF, whereas biomechanics only recognises 3DOF.

- The 3DOF used in biomechanics are: surge, sway and yaw to provide movement in a sagittal, frontal and transverse plane that fits in with the Cartesian coordinate system.

- Although biomechanics recognises 3DOF for global movements, most joint movements are reduced to a single degree of freedom.

- Biomechanics does not recognise the separation of the spine, hands or feet.

Thinking Cap

NB: Remember this Thinking Cap section contains straight forward questions. I am not trying to catch you out. As you read the questions just use your common sense to give a spontaneous answer. These are the basics and I am sure you as the reader can think of more questions that highlight the issues we face by continuing to use biomechanics, without opening up alternative movement theory possibilities.

1.   If there are more that 3DOF in the body then where does this leave us with regards to our current biomechanical map of the body?

2.   Do we just move in one of the three predicable ways?

3.   Are even 6DOF truly enough within a system to represent human movement? Especially when taking into consideration the vast individuality we all show whilst carrying out the same global activities?

4.   Are we not a deformable system?

5.   Are the physical systems of the body isolated from other systems with no interaction between systems? If for example, part a) has 6 parts, part b) has 4 parts, part c) has 6 parts etc., what happens when they all get combined?

6. What do we gain by reducing the complex down to produce a mathematically simplified equation?

Chapter 9

The body model

"Our scientific age demands that we provide definitions, measurements, and statistics in order to be taken seriously. Yet most of the important things in life cannot be precisely defined or measured."

- Dennis Prager

The reference points for range of motion, such as age, sex, height, dimensions of limbs etc. are taken from biomechanical anthropometry, which originated from physical, static anthropology. Anthropology seeks to describe the physical dimensions of the human body. The measurements are fixed, taken over short time scales and done at rest. These static measurements (static being not moving or from a cadaver) could include the segment (limb) length or link length, as well as its circumference. There is also the assumption that there is one centre-of-mass, which is the point where the entire objects mass is situated, at a solitary point.

The cadaver approach

The English anatomist Henry Gray (1827 – 1861) is famed for his detailed anatomy textbook; Gray's Anatomy. Along with his colleague Henry Vandyke, in 1855 Gray decided to produce an accessible textbook of anatomy for medical students. With Gray as the author and Vandyke as the illustrator the duo set about dissecting unclaimed bodies from hospitals mortuaries and workhouses, under the Anatomy Act (1832). The first edition was published in 1858 under the title Anatomy: Descriptive and Surgical and later Gray's Anatomy: Descriptive and Applied, before being shortened in later additions to Gray's Anatomy. Widely acclaimed and respected, Gray's Anatomy is considered a highly influential body of work on the subject of anatomy and has been updated, revised and continually in print since its original publication in 1858.

Hooke's spring

Robert Hooke (1635 – 1703) was a physicist, natural philosopher and polymath. He defined a principle of physics known as Hooke's law, which is a spring theory. Hooke's law states that "as the extension, so the force" or "the extension is proportional to the force", meaning that the forces needed to extend or compress a mechanical spring by a given distance are proportional to that distance and the spring remains stiff and always returns to its original and identical shape. Hooke's law is equated through linear approximation of the applied forces that are affecting the spring's stiffness. Hooke's law is applied where an elastic body can be deformed and if Hooke's equation is applicable to a material or elastic body it is described as Hookean or linear-elastic.

Hookean law and its materials have a direct linear relationship between stress and strain where biological tissue has a non-linear stress and strain curve. Hookean laws are applicable to man-made materials, which become weaker when they become stressed and according to Hookean law, they then become deformed and break. This suggests that Hookean laws apply to materials that work under low strain and in turn less energy is returned back to the structure; the opposite of biological tissue.

All biological tissues are nonlinear, incompressible and have non-Newtonian, and viscoelastic properties. Materials that exhibit viscous and elastic characteristics when undergoing deformation also exhibit a non-linear response to strain rate. These materials are categorized as adhering to non-Newtonian principles and is based upon a non-Hookean solid. Biological structures can resist much higher energy strains and actually become stiffer and stronger, not weaker as force is increased. This increase in strength and stiffness has a greater return of energy, as flexibility remains stable, enabling a greater expansion of energy over a much wider area. This wider expansion of energy means that there is never true balance in the material or structure and unlike material that complies with Hookean law, never returns exactly back to the original force and position. This expansion of force with higher strain rate and non-linear curve gives a suggestion that the structure gets thicker and bigger when the force is applied in biological tissue. In comparison with Hookean law based materials, which get thinner under a low strain with the structure breaking when the strength is at its weakest.

How is the anthropometric model used in biomechanics?

The amount of movement at any joint is an important diagnostic and treatment tool in biomechanics; it underpins what is classified as being normal and what is not. This is then produced as a gold standard set of numbers, which biomechanists use to document and suggest areas of improvement for performance.

Hooke's spring principle is used in biomechanics to understand the movement of biological tissue in the human body. Biomechanics uses this linear elastic model, which is the mathematical study of how solid objects become stressed due to prescribed loading conditions and is a simplification of elasticity and linear relationships between the components of stress and strain. In addition linear elasticity is valid only for stress states that do not produce yielding, which is the point of stress at which a material begins to deform. So for a material to be linear elastic it must not be able to deform, change shape or have non-linear forces applied to it.

The Hookean model suggests that the material changes length, with strain directly proportional to the forces being applied. This is the stress, which will occur over a linear relationship. This would be appropriate for a man-made material as they become weaker and thinner when stretched and bulge when compressed. If the material is stressed beyond a point it will break at the yield point. This suggests that the optimal range of stress is low strain levels, as well as being limited to one-dimensional geometry. Obviously, this is still not adequate for viscoelastic biological tissue.

Biological tissue gets stronger, stiffer and thicker when stretched and thinner when compressed with the optimal range being that over large strains. This makes sense as this returns a greater amount of energy back into the numerous structures; the strain is increased as well as not being restricted by the variations in the movements carried out by the individual.

According to Hookean theory the size, shape, design and mass of the creature involved needs to be the same as well as the strength and stiffness of bone involved. For example, every animal, including man human beings would need to be an identical clone for the theory to be applicable. Hooke's law fails once the forces exceeds a certain limit, since it is suggested that no material can be compressed beyond a certain point, or stretched beyond a maximum size, without some permanent deformation or change of state. In fact, many materials will noticeably deviate from Hooke's law well before those elastic limits are reached.

Hooke's law is an accurate approximation for solid bodies that are rigid for this reason. However, if any animal is different form the next, with differing size and mass etc. being slightly bigger from the predetermined norm then according to Hookean law the animals bones would fracture. On a mechanical structure this makes perfect sense as things are made exactly the same over and over again, whereas the individuality of a biological system is not compatible with Hooke's law.

So what's the problem?

Anthropometric data is based upon information taken from usually dead, static bodies or living static body's usually lying down to document the "average human" and provide a guide of average human dimensions. These simplified measurements provide an estimated universal number, which provides a basis for repeatable mathematics. This one size fits all model gives an estimate of what is normal and what is not.

How can this individual data correlate to the wider population and be used as the basis for making predications and estimations with a universal set of machine based mathematical calculations? It does this by truncating the numbers, which reduces the individual elements into sets. The numbers that work and fit within the mathematical equation are used, those that are random or chaotic are discarded. These are seen as outliers and are not used. These represent the true numbers of the data, as they represent the random nature of life. This is the representation of the body through statistics.

Though we will not go into statistics in depth here, it is always wise to remember statistics are looking for predictability and deterministic numbers so any data that does not fit the predictable pattern is called an outlier and is taken out from the analysis. This means that the 'relevant' data is grouped together and represented as one, whilst neglecting data that suggests something different from the same sample group and their different variables.

There is no doubt that the study of cadavers is an invaluable scientific tool when it comes to the area of medicine. However, there is an obvious problem when using the study of dead bodies to analyse how live bodies move; a cadaver is not moving. With function taken out of the picture a cadaver can help with some of the pieces of the puzzle but it does not tell you how a live body moves. Using a purely anatomical based approach leads to biological modelling that is based on dissection of inert, dead tissue.

My own personal view based on my understanding and belief about the human body and human movement, is that the body is a connected system. There is no start or end; our body is a living, breathing example of true holism. Everything from the visible, outer layer of the body down through to the skeleton is connected. So when a cadaver is used and a knife starts cutting, the interpretation of what is going on, is based on parts isolated from the whole. Essentially the direction that the knife cuts in will create a different picture of the human body.

Of course, biological tissue cannot follow the current biomechanical model of Hooke's law of elasticity. If biological tissue were Hookean it would not be able to move in a feely integrated way. Everything under Hookean law always works in a predicable linear way, requiring an external force to start its reaction. Once this force slows, which it does over the distance of the spring motion ceasing, Hookean law indicates that the spring will always returns perfectly back to the original start position. There is no change in shape at all.

What is clearly needed is a new model to replace the cadaver, anthropometric, spring based model that now dominates the thinking of biomechanics in regards to body measurements and tissue analysis. Maybe we can start by looking at functional, living, moving bodies where the combined action of any of the parts yields something other than the sum of the parts; where there is emergence of new properties or synergies.

Pit Stop Summary

- Anthropology describes physical dimensions of the body, with the measurement having been taken from a static body or cadaver.

- Hooke's law is used in biomechanics to understand movement of tissue and tissue elasticity.

- Cadavers are used in attempt to understand live bodies and have a better understanding on the workings of the internal body.

Thinking Cap

NB: Remember this Thinking Cap section contains straight forward questions. I am not trying to catch you out. As you read the questions just use your common sense to give a spontaneous answer. These are the basics and I am sure you as the reader can think of more questions that highlight the issues we face by continuing to use biomechanics, without opening up alternative movement theory possibilities.

1. Do you think anthropometric measurements and Hooke's law accurately represent the human body and human movement?

2. How can you predict the future when there is randomness?

3. How can we predict the future based on estimations that don't take into consideration important outliers?

4. Does individuality not matter?

5. Why do we need to simplify data?

6. Are the outliers not areas of true individuality?

7. Can we use the information taken from dead bodies in an attempt to represent living, moving human beings?

8.   Is it correct to use a one size fits all model based on static, non-moving body positions, to represent all 7 billion humans on this planet?

9.   Can a mathematical representation of a gold standard be the way to represents humans?

10.   Can the artificial constraints of a mechanical idea like a spring be a true representation of a biological structure?

Chapter 10

The alternative view

"The world hates change, yet it is the only thing that has brought progress".

- Charles Kettering

So far we have explored the history of biomechanics, taking a look at how the subject has evolved, how it is used today and the problem associated between classical mechanics and free natural human movement. With obvious differences between the model of 'man as a machine', verses complex human movement, it stands to reason that some people have strived to find an alternative model. Currently, there is only one alternative model that is in use in the movement world. Tensegrity. Although not accepted or even acknowledged by the biomechanical community, tensegrity is mainly embraced by the yoga, Pilates and osteopathy communities, as well as some forward or alternative thinking movement practitioners and rehabilitation specialists.

Where did tensegrity come from?

The term tensegrity was coined by Buckminster Fuller (1895 – 1983) by combining the words tension and integrity. He developed this word after being demonstrated a principle that the highly original and influential sculptor, Kenneth Snelson had discovered. Kenneth Snelson (b. 1927) is an American artist and sculptor and has created famous sculptures composed of rigid and flexible components that conform to the principle of tensegrity. Richard Buckminster Fuller was an American architect, author and systems theorist. Buckminster Fuller and Snelson met in 1948 when Fuller had taken an architect teaching position at a college that Snelson attended. In 1949 Snelson showed Fuller an example of his work that Snelson prefers to describe as "floating compression". Snelson's structures demonstrated discontinuous pressure and continuous tension and he has described the principle behind his work as "forces made visible".

Fuller is often credited with the invention of tensegrity but it was in fact his student, Snelson and his sculpture work that inspired the concept, which Fuller then named tensegrity. Or in other words, Fuller provided the commercialisation of the concept and coined the term tensegrity based on Snelson's original work. Because of this, Snelson is thought of by some as the true father of tensegrity.

What is tensegrity?

Tensegrity is known as tensional integrity or floating compression and is a structural principle based on the concept that the integrity of the structure comes from the balance of tension rather than compression. In a tensegrity model, isolated components in compression (struts or bars), float inside a net of continuous tension, without touching each other, with tensioned members delineating the system spatially (cables). The integrity of most man-made structures relies on a continuity of compression. For example, think of a house from the roof all the way down to the foundations where compressions runs in an uninterrupted line. Our bodies are often thought of in the same way as a stacking system, with bones, stacked on top of each other. However, tensegrity paved the way for an alternative model.

Tensegrity as the manufactured word suggests implies the structural system is characterized by the continuity of its tensile components. The main requirement of tensegrity, which has not changed since the time the concept was introduced, is that the system consists of distinct tensile and compressive components. The large majority of structural systems reported to date as being "tensegrities" are discrete pin-jointed networks.

There are three main categories of tensegrity structures:

1.   First category - the isolated components of compression are based on a single bar or strut that do not touch each other and are connected to a tension member (i.e.

cable) at a fixed point. These create a triangles, pentagons and hexagons and are rigid with fixed joints ensuring stability across the structure.

2. Second category - the isolated components of compression are based on two bars or struts that contact each other at their points, through a fixed fulcrum and lever, which is connected to a tension member (i.e. cable). This creates the same shape as in the first category but with a greater reinforcement to the shape.

3. Third category – the isolated components of compression are based on three bars or struts that contact each other at their points, through a fixed fulcrum and lever, which is connected to a tension member (i.e. cable).

A tensegrity structure in essence is made up of elements in compression and elements in tension, arranged in a hierarchical, self-organizing, energy efficient way. Although a tensegrity model is able to be manipulated, it will always revert back to its perfect, original shape. Deformation, shearing, bending, twisting, lengthening or change in shape from its original position do not occur in a tensegrity model.

How does tensegrity fit into our bodies? The birth of Biotensegrity.

Tensegrity is considered by some as the architecture of life, providing a set of building rules for complex constructions. Tensegrity has gathered interest in recent years as a workable alternative to the conventional and problematic system of biomechanics and is considered by many as a more logical model when looking at functional anatomy.

The application of tensegrity into a biological structure is an area of research credited to Dr Stephen Levin. As an orthopaedic surgeon, Dr Levin found through his work that joints do not compress each other but rather that our bones 'float' within a matrix of soft tissue. By taking the structural design of tensegrity, Dr Levin has used the principles to describe the relationship between the parts making up the organism and the organism as a whole and functional unit.

The scientific theory behind Levin's revolutionary work builds a unique set of principles to create a far superior working model to the current, mainstream, existing beliefs and teachings in regards to biomechanics and human anatomy. Levin's work advocates an integrated model of the human body that demonstrates the whole rather than individual parts. Biotensegrity offers a more efficient, no-lever approach to anatomy, in comparison with the current mechanistic view. This field of work is opening up a different kind of research into anatomy and movement and is getting people thinking outside the box.

So what's the problem?

Although tensegrity and the evolution of biotensegrity appear to be offering something completely different to orthodox biomechanics, on closer inspection there are some underlying issues when we take an engineering principle and try to fit it into the human body.

Firstly, tensegrity is still based upon Euclidean geometry, Newtonian mathematics and platonic solids, which are congruent faces of regular polygons, with the same number of faces meeting at each vertex. In order for a tensegrity to exist, it must comply with a set of geometrical constants which are characterized by a fixed or stationary condition showing little or no change. Five solids meet those criteria:

1) Triangle

2) Square

3) Pentagon

4) Hexagon

5) Octagon

These five solids each have joints acting like a revolute joint (also called a pin joint or a hinge joint), which has one degree of freedom. The solitary degree of freedom found in a pin joint provides repeatable and deterministic shapes that will always return to the original position, providing a constant. As we know this does not occur in nature; as nature and motion are ever changing and never constant, repeatable or deterministic. If this were the case, nature and life would not change or evolve.

These perfect geometric designs of a tensegrity concept, based on platonic solids later gave way to geodesic designs; which are straight lines attempting to fit a curved surface, quantified by liner geometry mathematics, based upon the Cartesian coordinate system. Geodesic shapes, from a tensegrity perspective are at the foundation of all nature and life. In order to design a tensegrity model, solid platonic shapes (e.g. triangles) are added together to form a bigger or different geometrical platonic shape, with more faces and vectors built upon the first shape. These faces and vectors are essentially an enlargement of the original shape. The faces are a flat shape representation of the full shape and the vectors are the straight lines from one point to another, brought to life from a flat picture on a piece of paper to an artificial shape of balance configurations via computational mathematics.

A tensegrity structure has invisible forces, which can be any force that exists in nature. A tensegrity model is quantified by the principles of mechanical forces as the structure has to maintain its geometrical shape, which then must function in any position. It will achieve this by having natural frequencies, which are always finding balance. This idea of no shape change means there is no adaption as the structure always reverts back exactly to its original design, which makes it fixed and deterministic.

Aside from the definition that a tensegrity structure is made up of elements in compression and tension, there is no true definition about the nature of these components. The components of tensegrity were founded by a single idea from one individual and are still spoken about in the same context today. This original information was designed for and around mechanical engineering and mechanical sculptures. There is nothing at all about the existence and nature of the components e.g. soft, deformable, flexural etc. This in turn makes the description of tensegrity bias based on a single individuals (and later others who continued the work) perception and interpretation of a mechanical structure.

Because tensegrity is not a term that has been absolutely defined, the interpretation of the topic is wide. When looking at a model to represent the human body it should be all encompassing. However, this appears not to be the case as the major influences on tensegrity are based upon the knowledge as a structural, engineering principle. We understand tensional integrity as a principle based upon components in compression and continuous tension, where the compressed struts do not touch each other and the pre-stressed tensioned members, delineate the system spatially. However, this is not an all-encompassing understanding as there is no definition or understanding about things such as pressure, fluid, electrical, magnetic and deformational forces, which can all provide tension and compression from a different perspective.

The following also highlights more problems with the explanation of tension and compression in the tensegrity model in relation to the human body:

- Tensegrity structures contain struts that always remain isolated.

- Tension and compression cables and struts never touch.

- Compression struts contact each other at their ends through fixed fulcrums and levers.

- Tension and compressional forces are separated.

Another major factor is that in a tensegrity structure, the cables cannot withstand compression and the struts cannot withstand tension. Therefore the stress in a cable must be non-negative and the stress in a strut must be non-positive; resulting in perfect balance, characterized once again by linear components in a fixed or stationary condition, showing little or no continuing change. This is turn suggests that:

1. Loading members are only in pure compression or pure tension, meaning the structure will fail if any components reverse their design.

2. The mechanical stability, which allows the members to remain in either tension or compression results in perfect equilibrium. This is when the net force on that structure is

zero and no true motion is occurring as this system is still mechanical in nature.

A mathematical set of principles are used within the definition of a tensegrity. This set of principles is that of a set of finite configuration of points, called the nodes, positioned in a Cartesian coordinate system, where some pairs of the nodes are designated cables, constrained not to get further apart, and some pairs are designated struts, constrained not to get closer together. This suggests that tensegrity is only applicable and represented when using a finite mathematical set of principles. Based on points and balance conforming to geometrical shapes of Euclid and in turn the classical mathematics of Newton.

Statics is a set of mechanical principles that are concerned with the conditions under which bodies remain at rest irrespective of their surroundings. These bodies are then in a state of equilibrium, with all forces balanced out. Forces such as traditional tension and compression fall into this category, which are acting at one point through lines called vectors. Because there is balance and equilibrium there is no motion and this is a problem associated with Newton's first law of uniform straight line motion, as it is hard to separate the differences between motion and rest.

It is good to remember that classical physics determines that all of life follows these classical laws and all of life is moving towards a state of balance. Balance is equal and not moving, not changing or adapting. Our new laws and theory of human movement should describe how motion moves away from a state of balance, only to interact with other states of imbalance, resulting in a moment in time where balance is occurring as it passes through these imbalances. All of life and any structure are never returning to an original position or shape as this imbalance is deforming everything.

Essentially, tensegrity is still a static engineering principle, which will always be problematic when attempting to transfer into a natural human body to represent human movement. The current views still only uses the original knowledge of tensegrity that was based upon innate objects.

Biotensegrity in so many ways is a completely fresh approach to beating down the same path with outdated ideologies that we explored in the first part of this book. Dr Steven Levin has set the tone for the evolution of how we think about, describe and teach functional anatomy. The no-levers approach is something to be pursued and the evolution on the subject is helping to break down the barriers of the past and move the theory of anatomy and movement into the future. However, in my opinion there is still a long way to go until we have a working theory of anatomy and movement that accurately represents the reality of our bodies and the way we move.

Pit Stop Summary

- The term tensegrity is a blend between the words tension and integrity.

- The term was coined by Richard Buckminster Fuller based upon the work of sculptor, Kenneth Snelson.

- A tensegrity structure is an engineering model that has struts in compression and cables in tension to allow it to stabilize itself.

- Tensegrity is based on Euclidian geometry, Newtonian mathematics and platonic solids.

- Geodesic shapes, underpin tensegrity structures, which always revert back to their original position and design and are therefore fixed and deterministic.

- There is no true definition in tensegrity about the nature of the components, aside from the elements in compression and tension.

- Biotensegrity is the evolution of the principles of tensegrity into biology and is an area of research credited to Dr Stephen Levin.

- Biotensegrity advocates a theoretical model of the body that is an integrated and an efficient whole, without levers. A great step forwards from the current, existing biomechanical model.

- However, biotensegrity still uses the foundation that tensegrity is built upon; essentially a static engineering principle, which will always be problematic when attempting to transfer the model into a natural human body to represent human movement.

Thinking Cap

NB: Remember this Thinking Cap section contains straight forward questions. I am not trying to catch you out. As you read the questions just use your common sense to give a spontaneous answer. These are the basics and I am sure you as the reader can think of more questions that highlight the issues we face by continuing to use biomechanics, without opening up alternative movement theory possibilities.

1. Are we linear biological systems?

2. Do our bodies exhibit definite characteristics, outside the tensegrity model of compression and tension?

3. Are our bodies made up of Euclidian shapes?

4. Can the human body be accurately mapped by an innate engineering principle?

5. Are we deterministic, non-deformable creatures?

6. Are we always in a state of balance?

7. Are we always static and constant in the way we move?

8. Is our movement predetermined?

Part 3. The Future

Human biomechanics: where is the theory of human movement going?

Chapter 11

The movement theory revolution

"It's like an artist with a clean slate. You just have to paint a new picture. And hopefully a better one".

- Brian Mollare

Movement theory – where are we now and where are we going?

It is important to remember that looking at biomechanics and offering vastly different alternatives is a completely new undertaking. The introduction of this information is the beginning of a much deeper path to travel. I am positive that each day more and more views and theories will be added and eventually a new, widely accepted paradigm of movement theory will evolve. Although the theory is obviously not the practice and we can 'do' without any of the scientific understanding, analysing or studying of the theory of movement. It is my opinion that by creating a consistent, realistically representative theory of movement will only serve to enhance our understanding and allow current and future practitioners, movement scientists and rehabilitation experts to be able to unite in a coherent expression of the their findings, treatment and analysis of human movement.

As we have explored, biomechanics uses classical laws and mathematics to simplify the representation of human movement. Using mathematics provides order, precise formulas, quantitative results and predictions or solutions based on repeatable, estimated patterns. Advances in computation technology based on mathematics has made biomechanics an active area of research. However, all of these software programs essentially break movement down into a very simplified model, with the underlying principle that 'man is a machine'.

If we as movers, practitioners, therapists, movement scientists, coaches or rehabilitation experts do not believe that the 'man as machine' model is best serving our understanding of human movement then what realistic alternatives to biomechanics do we have available?

As we have seen in the previous section, the furthest evolutionary branch of this area of research thus far is Dr Levin's work on biotensegrity. However, as we have seen all areas of research into human movement are currently all mechanistic in nature, based on engineering principles of inanimate objects and when traced back all rely on Euclidian shapes and Newtonian mathematics. Euclidian shapes are only mathematical concepts and not real life things, as they are mathematical abstractions and simplifications, which are easy for mechanics to use to fit a predetermined hypothesis.

This view comes with all the associated problems explored

in the first section of this book. So I guess it comes down to this: can our movement, as animate human beings be summed up with a mechanistic, engineering principles, using predictable mathematical equations suited for inanimate objects? I am hoping, that like me, you can see the problem of where we are right now. All of our models of movement use a chronological science that we can trace back to Euclid, over 2400 years ago. Of course science and technology have evolved but instead of looking for a new approach that more realistically represents anatomy and human movement we are trying to evolve our existing theories and science based on outdated machine ideologies.

If as movement experts we trace back to the roots and identify the issues at the foundation of the subject, then maybe we have a chance of challenging the existing situation and moving into a new paradigm of understanding. So from everything we have explored what is the main problem? In my opinion, it's actually really simple. The problem is in the maths. The whole time we are focused on a mathematical, quantitative approach to movement theory and understanding, we are inhibiting any potential growth in the subject.

All of the previous scientific theories of human movement all have mathematics in common. Biotensegrity does not use mathematics directly but does use principles of tensegrity, which in turn relies on Newtonian mathematics. By having to revert back to a set of systems that are only applicable for machines and then finding a number to fit this hypothesis we are often missing the essence of human movement. Currently, in the theory of human movement, maths makes the model. For example, you have an idea, which you then need to quantify and then design a mathematical equation that simplifies the model, only using numbers that fit the hypothesis. Numbers that do not fit the hypothesis are frequently neglected in attempt to produce a simplified model or number that represents the selected hypothesis. When in fact, the numbers that have been neglected, may be the numbers that show the more complex individuality but cannot be included as they do not fit the hypothesis.

A clean slate

Currently, there is no model of movement that accurately reflects what happens in the human body as we move. So instead of just tracing back as a movement scientist, is it possible to draw a new map that more accurately represents the terrain of human movement? If we take out the mathematics; draw a clean slate, then where does it leave us? Hopefully, with a chance of creating a theory of movement that matches up to the outstanding level of practical work going on the globe.

This is a problem that I run into time and time again. There are many advanced practitioners of different methods in the international community but their practical work is not justified by the current biomechanical thinking. It is my hope that by rewriting the theory and rules of human movement that we can gain a deeper scientific understanding of the real nature of movement and provide credibility to a whole host of principles, methods and movement practices. People who practice can often vouch for 'their method' working and have seen consistent results with their client base but science does not necessarily verify the efficacy of their method, because the map is missing that particular street.

A new way

If we take mathematics out of the model of movement then we are curing some of the issues that we face with trying to force the reality of human movement into the biomechanical mould. It is my strong belief that we require a brand new way of speaking about, describing, presenting on, learning about and understanding the way our bodies move.

So what will the updated road map of human movement look? The alternative view of biomechanics is a completely new area of research but one that I feel is long overdue. I do not have the complete road map ready for you to view and I do not claim to have all the answers but in this chapter I intend to lay out the main prerequisite components of what our updated theory of human movement science should incorporate.

The modern theory of human movement: the prerequisite components

Holism - Holism is derived from the Greek word 'olos', meaning all or whole. The concept of holism is an understanding that complex systems are made up of interconnected parts that are not able to be understood or exist independently from each other. The whole system is considered to be greater than the sum of its parts and the system should be viewed as a cohesive whole rather than reduced to its parts. Reductionism is considered the opposite of holism and is the approach of understanding a complex system by analysing and reducing the system to the workings of isolated parts.

The principles of holism mean that a system can be examined at the level of principles governing the behaviour of the whole system and not at the level of the structure and behaviour of its component parts. Biomechanics on the other hand uses a reductionist approach, which takes a complex system and reduces it to the level of the structure and behaviour of its component parts. The following are three main cornerstones of holism:

1. A holistic system is more than the sum of its basic physical parts.

2. The system exhibits properties that are not purely determined by its physical parts.

3. The system obeys laws that are not solely determined by the structure and behaviour of its physical parts.

A holistic approach is akin with the theory of quantum entanglement, which is where all interactions cannot be described independently. Holism is also synonymous with organicism, which is the perspective that systems and their parts are organic wholes rather than being made of individual parts that are isolated from each other.

Complex systems - A complex system represents a new approach to science that investigates how relationships between parts give rise to the collective behaviours of a system and how the system interacts and forms relationships with its environment.

Systems theory and systems biology - Systems theory is the study of systems with the aim of finding patterns and elucidating principles. Systems biology is a sub category of systems theory that draws on bioscience research and focuses on the complex interactions in biological systems with the underlying principle of holism rather than reductionism.

Non-liner system - In contrast to a linear system, a nonlinear system does not satisfy the superposition principle; or in other words a nonlinear system is a chaotic and unpredictable system where the output is not directly proportional to the input.

Synergistics - Synergy comes from the Greek word 'sinergos' meaning working together. Synergy creates a greater whole than the sum of its parts and is the empirical study of systems in transformation, with emphasis on total system behaviour that is not predictable based on the behaviour of any isolated components.

Emergence - Emergence is the process where smaller, more simple entities interact to create larger entities, more complex entities or patterns that exhibit properties that were not seen prior to emergence. For example, the very process of life is considered an emergent property of molecules interacting.

Self-organisation - This is a process where local components in a disordered system interact to form some kind of global order or coordination, which arises spontaneously from within the system itself. Cybernetics is the approach for exploring the systems structures and possibilities to organise itself in the best possible state for the circumstances with an underlying principle of behavioural flexibility, meaning the understanding that an organism can do something new.

Sub-optimisation - Sub optimisation is a process where the system does not have to be perfect in order to thrive within the environment and provides the best possible outcome to produce increased efficiency within the structure. Sub-optimisation is akin with the principle of intelligent choice, which is the idea that an organism chooses the best outcome in any situation.

Non-Mathematical Topology - Topology is the area of study concerned with the properties of space and shape that can deform through stretching, bending and twisting.

Vitalism - Vitalism is a theory that states "living organisms are fundamentally different from non-living entities because they contain some non-physical element or are governed by different principles than are inanimate things" (Betchel, William and Robert C. Richardson).

Holonomic system - Is a system that is an evolving self-organizing aspect and whose structures and systems that attempt to exist at a balance point between chaos and order and one which is not determined by physical laws underpinning the structure and behaviour of their basic physical parts.

Morphological elasticity - An organism has the potential to change its form in attempt to find the best organised state or outcome for the situation.

Pit Stop Summary

- Biomechanics uses classical laws and maths to simplify human movement.

- By focusing on quantitative data, movement is reduced to a predictable and repeatable pattern.

- The furthest evolutionary branch of the theory of real life human motion is biotensegrity, but this is still approached from an engineering perspective.

- There is no model that accurately reflects how we as human beings move.

- Often there is a huge gap between the practical work going on at an outstandingly high level around the world and the theory or science behind it. It's time to bridge the gap.

- I propose we take maths out of the equation and start to focus our attention on a more qualitative approach to human movement.

- I believe the principle components the new theory of movement are based upon are: holism, complex systems, systems theory and systems biology, non-linear systems, synergistics, emergence, self-organisation, sub-optimisation, non-mathematical topology, holonomic systems and morphological elasticity.

Thinking Cap

NB: Remember this Thinking Cap section contains straight forward questions. I am not trying to catch you out. As you read the questions just use your common sense to give a spontaneous answer. These are the basics and I am sure you as the reader can think of more questions that highlight the issues we face by continuing to use biomechanics, without opening up alternative movement theory possibilities.

1. As a mover, practitioner, therapist, movement scientist, coach or rehabilitation expert do you feel that the current theory of movement accurately reflects what you feel, see and experience in your own body and/or your clients bodies?

2. Looking at movement theory as an overview, taking into consideration the origins of the subject is there a way of evolving our current theory or is it time to draw a line and take a different approach more in context with our twenty first century understanding of human movement?

3. Is the mechanistic viewpoint and comparison to humans being like a machine not just a metaphor and hypothesis, based on engineering principles? If so why can we not re-write the hypothesis from a more biological based perspective?

4. Does your understanding of current movement theory work to support and justify your practical application of movement?

5. Do you think our human bodies as holistic, complex, non-linear systems that work synergistically, whilst exhibiting properties of emergence, self-organisation and efficiency?

Chapter 12

Integral compliancy

"What's my philosophy? In a word, integral."

- Ken Wilbur

As we explored earlier, biomechanics advocates the link man, made up of isolated linked parts. The new theory of movement needs to move away from the isolated links to the whole. The bigger, more integrated picture.

Integral compliance is the term I have used to describe the idea that the body is a compliant structure. This means that it is a single-piece flexible structure, with both mobility and rigidity being transferred through both semi-rigid and soft elements, to create an action, depending upon what is required at any given moment.

As already highlighted a conventional rigid-link mechanism is comprised of a number of discrete links connected by kinematic joints. The mobility in a mechanism such as this is obtained from the relative rigid-body motion between links, due to the reduced degrees of freedom available at the joints. In reality biological systems are designed to be non-rigid and supple structures to sustain and transfer the energy generated from both internal and external forces. To do this the body must be free of the restrictions imposed by the degrees of freedom currently used in biomechanical analysis. The integrally compliant system functions as a transmission between the activated input and the output. But instead of deriving its mobility from the relative rigid-body motion between links that a machine principle uses, a compliant system utilizes the structural deformation, induced by an input actuation, to transmit force or deliver motion.

Joint spaces

In a biomechanical model the link man analysis is broken by a series of joints. I am advocating that this model does not serve our understanding as it reinforces isolation. I prefer to think of joints as joint spaces rather that links, which provides a channel for force to be transferred through. This means than two bones do not directly touch. The only two bones that do are inside the ear. As two bones do not touch, the traditional theory of a joint as outlined in the lever man principle is outdated. Rather than a fixed point, the joint becomes a space, allowing the bones which are situated within this space to move independently from each other and in any direction. This joint space by virtue of the bones movement, produces a stress on the surrounding biological tissue, which is vital for the new understanding of human movement.

Due to the absence of joints or links, a compliant

mechanism can also be seen as a structure that is stiff enough to bear loads but supple enough to transfer force throughout the structure. In a machine link system, deformation is not desirable, whereas in a compliant system the structural deformation is now considered a desirable effect, providing mobility to work against the external loads. In other words, a compliant system is a combination of a structure that can become both soft and rigid depending on the variations of pressure, from fluid and air changes.

What exactly does the term 'compliant system' mean when used to describe the human body?

I am advocating the term compliant system to mean that the body is a single-piece, flexible, joint-less structure that gains its mobility from structural deformation due to an input actuation. It is a monolithic (single-piece) device that is capable of doing what conventional systems can do with multiple links and hinges. It is also designed to be flexible enough to transmit motions, yet stiff enough to withstand external loads. The compliant system can be classified as having both thick and thin flexural segments that mimic the revolute joints seen in rigid link mechanisms but are not jointed like revolute joints, as they move with many changes in shape through the non-restriction of freedom, rather than in one degree of freedom.

The localized deformation due to bending at these flexural

segments provides the required mobility in the compliant mechanism. The mobility of the compliant system is derived from the structural deformation that is more evenly distributed over the entire structure. A compliant system can essentially be seen as a traditional mechanism with flexural components replacing the rigid link and revolute joints.

Due to its hinge-less nature, an integrally compliant system offers numerous advantages over traditional mechanisms, as it reduces the number of parts needed within its system. The ability to store strain energy in compliant mechanisms eliminates the need of fixed parts; the monolithic feature eliminates joints and connections, replacing the body with joint spaces and producing a lighter and more expansive structure. In addition, the absence of traditional joints greatly simplifies the movement. The body works as an anti-gravitational system on the inside, which provides its expansive and malleable structure. This in combination with the gravity on the outside of the system provides the required pressure changes, which occur internally to match the gravitational pressure on the outside. It is this change in the compliant system that is the start of the true meaning of the non-link man and in turn, a new understanding of the biological form.

A compliant system transforms motion or power. It can also provide power internally as well as externally. This is another major component missing from a rigid mechanics model. In a compliant system power is generated by the manipulation, deflection and deformation of a flexible structure, enabling it to store energy in the form of strain energy. Strain energy is an elastic potential produced in flexible structures as they transfer force to another point through elastic body manipulation, deflection and deformation, which changes the shape of the whole structure involved. This is unlike rigid-body mechanisms, where actuations are applied at the joints connecting the rigid members, with the structure needing some external force to start the action and force to continue to maintain the action. In a rigid-body mechanism, when the external force is taken away no action will occur.

Since a compliant structure is a single-piece structure there are no joints rubbing between two parts and friction as seen at the joints of a rigid body mechanisms is absent. This in turn does not reduce the energy in the system, which traditional mechanics does, resulting in energy draining from the system. Compliant systems are designed through the topology optimization of shape changing, which transfers or transforms motion, force, or energy. Unlike rigid-link mechanisms, however, compliant structures gain their mobility from the deflection of flexible members rather than from movable joints only.

A compliant system offers better reliance to overloading and shock absorbing, which we have to control on a daily basis and a better attenuation of vibrational forces. A traditional model cannot control the vibration we are constantly exposed to within the different frequency, amplification and oscillation spectrums. I propose the human organism must be a compliant system, made of a continuous sheet of flexibility, with the ability to be expanding and contracting at the same time providing stiffness and flexibility when the system requires it.

This change between a stiffness and flexibility in an elastic system, is described by myself as "deform motion", is not like uniform motion that is constant. Rather deform motion is a changing motion from one state to another, which provides the stability and mobility of the structures, dependent on the deformation allowed in the system. Classical laws do not allow for deformation and deformed motion.

A compliant system has it foundation in non-mathematical topology and topological shapes with the ability to be modelled as one piece, then changing to accommodate force and motion. Topology is a non-Euclidean geometry and is the study of the ever changing motions of shapes and spaces. It is an area concerned with the properties of space that are preserved under deformations including: stretching, twisting, pulling and bending but not tearing or gluing. Spatial relations are unaffected by the continuous change of shape or size of changes.

Elastic integration, is one of the main underlying principles of the body as a compliant structure. With the view that the elastic and deformation properties of the structure allow the elastic elements to integrate with all the other elastic elements, throughout the whole of the structure in an omnidirectional manner. This omnidirectional is wide, long, high, deep, close, narrow and in any direction and space that the structure occupies. It is a dynamic process where all internal structures have integrated pathways, within each other that are free from any constraints of direction, angle, space and position.

It is my firm standpoint that biological structures and motion are compliant systems; be it fascia, muscle, bone, ligaments, tendons, skin and nerves. If this were not the case, then change and motion would not occur.

The main advantages of an integrally compliant system are:

1.   No conventional joints, rather joint spaces

2.   No friction or wear if the structure is maintained

3.   Multiple configurations

4.   No assembly

Wormholes

A compliant structure is an interconnected structure that communicates with itself through its various connections. Where current mechanical principles has a linear view of isolated parts that only connect to the next isolated part in a chain without greater interconnection (for example, a) connects to b), b) connects to c) etc.). Whereas an integrated complaint structure has omnidirectional interconnections that are local, global, long, short, deep, wide and are of different shapes and sizes, creating a flexible and elastic system that can infold by itself and upon itself, in non-symmetrical topological loops, knots and spirals.

Because the compliant system is entwined and integrated, tension is created in some places and compression in others. It is these omnidirectional connections that is the true nature of biological tissue. Compliant systems is the essential dynamic process to explain the creation of dimensions, matter and energy.

Pit Stop Summary

Integral compliance describes the concept of the body as:

- being a single piece, flexible structure

- exhibiting signs of mobility and rigidity

- stiff enough to bear loads and supple enough to transfer force and vibration

- without joints

- gaining mobility through structural deformation

- a pressurised system

- without internal friction

- able to absorb and pass on vibrational forces

- a semi solid and elastic system

- based on topological shapes

Thinking Cap

NB: Remember this Thinking Cap section contains straight forward questions. I am not trying to catch you out. As you read the questions just use your common sense to give a spontaneous answer. These are the basics and I am sure you as the reader can think of more questions that highlight the issues we face by continuing to use biomechanics, without opening up alternative movement theory possibilities.

1. Does a link-man model accurately reflect human movement?

2. Could we gain more from a road-map of human bodies being integrated, supple, flexible, adaptive organisms?

3. Should we be looking at the body in isolation and trying to gain understanding about the whole based on the predictions of parts?

4. Or is it time to start understanding the bigger picture of human movement; with the perspective that the human body is a complete, whole structure that functions adhering to principles of adaptability, self-organisation and emergence?

5. Do our bodies need external force only to create movement?

6. If our bodies really operated in accordance with rigid body mechanics, would we be able to move at all?

Chapter 13

Biokinesis-ontology

"You never change things by fighting the existing reality. To change something, build a new model that makes the existing model obsolete."

- Richard Buckminster Fuller

What is Biokinesis-ontology?

I have termed the alternative to biomechanics and the new theory of movement biokinesis-ontology. Biokinesis-ontology is a portmanteau of the terms biology, kinesis and ontology:

- Biology is the scientific study of living organisms.

- Kinesis is the Greek word for movement or motion.

- Ontology is a branch of philosophical metaphysics concerned with the study of the nature of reality. Ontology is a prerequisite for physics and motion but does not need to take into consideration any mathematics associated with it. Ontology is about the initial idea but does not require mathematics to bring it to life. It is the study of physics that is ultimately concerned with descriptions of the real world, while mathematics is concerned with abstract patterns. Therefore, statements of physics contain theories, while mathematical statements are analytical and mathematical hypothesis are required to fit into a mould.

Biokinesis-ontology is based upon the theories of movement, the description of nature and the reality of the human organism. I believe we cannot ever hope to fully understand human movement purely in terms of the physical laws that are used in biomechanics, which are derived from the study of inanimate objects and systems. Biomechanics lives in the analytical or mathematical world. Essentially, where mathematics contains hypotheses; physics contains theories. With ontology, the philosophy itself stands alone without being bogged down in maths.

What does the map of Biokinesis-ontology look like?

By taking our research back to the human biological form based on the prerequisite components discussed in chapter 11 (holism, complex systems, systems theory and systems biology, non-liner system, synergistics, emergence, self-organisation, sub optimisation, non-mathematical topology, vitalism, holonomic systems and morphological elasticity), it becomes possible to look at the human body and human movement from a new perspective.

With the acceptance that the human body is an integrally compliant system instead of the underlying assumption and belief system that 'man is a machine' we can begin to draw a new picture and make a new model from the ground up about how our bodies move.

The concept of biokinesis-ontology is based around a term I call 'dynisation', meaning dynamic complex organisation of the workings of the human organism, and in turn its associated movements. The whole concept of biokinesis-ontology and this new area that I feel represents the human organism and movement is based on the foundation of holism.

The anti-gravity body

As spoken about in compliant systems, living organisms do not follow current biomechanical ideas. Another major missing component of biomechanics is hydrodynamics (fluid and air), which is a consideration that is completely absent from human biomechanics. Hydrodynamics offers a model of stability and mobility in the living body. One way this occurs is through hydrodynamic skeletons, where force is transmitted by internal pressure. This involves displacement of fluid from one location to another in order to change shape or exert force elsewhere, rather than stability occurring through rigid skeletal elements. This occurs through the anti-gravity body.

The anti-gravity body is an idea of an object or being that is free from the force of gravity and this concept is key to an integrally compliant structure. It does not refer to the lack of weight under gravity experienced in free fall like Newtonian gravitation, but rather it is achieved via an expansion and repulsion (not attraction and compression) of pressure force such as fluid or air pressures exerted within encasements. It applies this via viscoelastic, hydrodynamic and hydrostatic forces. For example, the human body is encased via the tissue and skin with a volume of enclosed fluid and gas.

Newtonian gravity is based upon the attraction of two visible objects of solid matter moving in uniform motion with nothing between these objects. By having nothing that interferes with the attraction of the objects it is seen to be in a closed system and isolated from the environment. But what about non-visible matter? Like energy waves obtained from vibration and other fictitious forces filling the medium of ether (space). This energy can either be in an attractive or repulsive state, where energy can move freely but at specific times become dampened and slowed down before it meets a second random energetic state. These energetic states may be in different forms like electrical, heat, sound and light to name a few. This randomness to the energy state will produce omnidirectional, anti-gravity like waves which are non-deterministic, meaning that future behaviour cannot be precisely predicted but will emerge in self-organisation to meet its goal. This omnidirectional set of interactions occurring within and between any objects gives the view that anti-gravity in a medium like the human body is a possibility.

I can hear you saying"...but of course there is gravity", and you would of course be correct in this reasoning. But what I am suggesting is that gravity is in effect externally from the body and for a different set of rules to apply internally. If your internal body worked like gravity suggests, as a pushing attraction to the centre of the earth, we would be flat on the floor. Evolution has taken us from fish in the sea, which is anti-gravity; to a quad pedal lizard on land with a horizontal spine, close to the floor; to a bipedal mammal standing with the spine vertical. If we were not an anti-gravity internal system we would still be in the sea.

The current gravitational model may be problematic externally as already explored in the Newton section but to use these rules for analysing inside the human body, which is a pressurised, anti-gravity system is highly problematic. It is the ever changing balance between the external gravity and the internal gravity that maintains the perfect imbalance of the system. If we produced a perfectly balanced system, that matched external gravity to internal anti-gravity, no motion could occur due to the forces equalling themselves out and we would result in a state of stillness. The gravitational theory that biomechanics currently uses is applied externally as well as internally, thus suggesting that everything would remain balanced, static and unable to evolve.

With the anti-gravity system things are in a state of imbalance, always trying to achieve balance without ever quite achieving it. This is the foundation of an ever changing, self-organising system that is always changing and evolving.

The presegrity system

Biological tissue is based upon nonlinear properties, which experience large deformations and a stress-strain relationship called viscoelasticity. If a material when undergoing deformation exhibits both viscous and elastic characteristics then this property is known as viscoelastic. Unlike the Hookean model of purely elastic substances, a viscoelastic substance has a viscous component in addition to an elastic component. The viscosity of a viscoelastic substance gives the substance a strain rate dependent on time and strain levels. A viscoelastic substance loses energy when a load is applied and returns it via heat through dynamic aero elasticity, whereas purely elastic materials do not dissipate heat (energy) when a load is applied and then removed.

Dynamic aero elasticity studies the interactions between the inertial, elastic, and aerodynamic forces that occur when an elastic body is exposed to a fluid flow brought about via the variables within the hydrodynamic model along with the dissipation of vibration, dampening noise, and absorbing shock. Functioning of the system depends on the fact that they are essentially constant in volume as they consist of relatively incompressible fluids and pressurised air tissue. Contraction of biological tissue and the resulting decrease in one of the dimensions thus results in an increase in another dimension. Whether tissue is active or passive, stiff or compliant, controls the various dimensions and a wide array of deformations, movements and changes in responses can be created.

A hydrodynamic skeleton includes a volume of enclosed fluid. This liquid has a high bulk modulus, which simply means that it resists significant volume change. The motion of the spiral articulations found in all biological tissue will decrease the diameter, thereby increasing the pressure, and because no significant change in volume can occur, this decrease in diameter must result in an increase in length. Following elongation, shortening can be caused by the constriction of the tissue at various positions, which changes the diameter providing the non-symmetrical spiral shapes seen in all biological structures. The function of the system thus depends on the pressurized internal fluid, gas and air.

Hydrodynamic skeletons lack the fulcrums and lever arms present in rigid skeletons as outlined in the compliant system, which allows amplification of force, displacement and velocity with there every changing shape, symmetry and size; providing a system for the amplification of movement via the pressurised system.

The walls of the hydrostatic skeleton is reinforced with layers of numerous connective fibres that control the mobility and stability of the structure. The fibres are typically arranged as a crossed-fibre spiral where sheets of connective tissue fibres wrap the structure in right and left directional, non-symmetrical spirals. These spirals allow for elongation and shortening, unlike the Hookean model of elasticity, as it controls the shape change, allowing for non-linear deformation to occur above the strain threshold.

Although hydrodynamic skeletons lack the rigid levers and fulcrum that provide mechanical amplification in rigid link man models, amplification can nevertheless still occur. The amplification is a simple consequence of the relationship between dimensional changes in a structure that is essentially constant in volume. The form of amplification seen in hydrostatic skeletons has some interesting implications for the evolution of biological tissue. Unlike the situation with the rigid link man model, where the displacement of tissue is amplified by the lever system and thus muscle strain is limited, the tissues in hydrostatic skeletons are subjected to larger strains, which gives back greater energy to the system making it very energy efficient. Energy efficiency is vital in the evolution of all nature and life.

Within the compliant system, the non-Newtonian model is semi solid, flexible and able to deform, due not only to the design but also due to the pressure created throughout the system. The human organism uses pressure to stiffen the body and as a result, the contraction of any part of the compliant system affects the rest, altering either length or tension. This serves a variety of functions in support and movement. For example, the skeleton transmits the force generated by tissue contraction, providing support for maintenance of posture and for movement and locomotion. Also, because tissue cannot actively elongate and pull due to the pressures changes occurring, the compliant system actually expands and tissue pushes, which is unlike the current muscle mode of compression and pulling. This serves to amplify the displacement, the velocity or the force through the compliant system and the force that is transmitted by internal pressure.

The function of the system thus depends on the pressurized internal fluid, which is essentially constant in volume, as it consists of relatively incompressible fluids and tissue. One possibility to consider regarding bones is that it is not their only primary role to move the structure but also to provide adequate space within tissue to maintain internal pressurised forces, which are within a balanced and subtle pressurised structure. This pressure system fluctuates depending upon the positions created by the vibration impacted upon the bone, which expands pressure into and upon the surrounding tissue; I have termed this as presegrity (pressure + integrity).

A very interesting aspect of presegrity structures (e.g. fluid, gas and air structures and their associated pressure) is that they have properties such as soft, light, flexible, multi-functional, as well as hard and stiff and the structure is optimized for self-organisation.

Alongside hydrodynamic skeletons is the concept of tissue hydrostat, where the tissue itself both creates movement and provides skeletal support for that movement. It can provide this support because it is composed primarily of an incompressible liquid and is thus constant in volume. The most important feature of tissue hydrostat is its constant volume. Tissue is composed primarily of an aqueous liquid that is essentially incompressible at physiological pressures. In a tissue hydrostat or any other structure of constant volume, a decrease in one dimension will cause a compensatory increase in at least one other dimension. The system of elongation, bending and spiral motion is dependent on constancy of volume to effect shape changes in the absence of rigid attachments.

An introduction to one of the major properties of substances within a hydrodynamic and hydrostat system is that of thixotropy; or in other words, a substance that's viscosity is time and/or temperature dependant. For example, this is the notion that a thick or viscous fluid under static conditions, will become thin, less viscous and start to flow over time when moved. The fluid will then take a fixed time to return to a more viscous state, which is the time lag between stability and mobility of the system.

Synovial fluid, cerebral spinal fluid and blood are thixotropic materials, exhibiting a stable form at rest but becoming fluid when agitated. Thixotropic fluids do not follow the laws of Newton, as Newtonian fluids follow the linear relationship between the shear stress and the shear rate passing directly through the origin. This is highlighted again in Hooke's laws of elasticity and the current view of stress and strain spoken about previously. Pressurised systems, hydrostatics and hydrodynamics, are systems that work with spaces and cavities within the body. A cavity in the body is any pressurised substance or fluid-filled space in a multicellular organism, other than those of vessels (such as blood vessels and lymph vessels), as well as cavities such as cranial, thoracic, abdominal, abdominal pelvic, pelvic and spinal cavities to name a few.

Synovial fluid, is a viscous, non-Newtonian fluid found in various cavities of the body, providing suction within a vacuum to reduce friction between the articular cartilage of synovial joints during movement. This vacuum has a sleeve (tissue membrane), which provides pressure within the joint and this force in the fluid pushes against the membrane. This pressure results in electric forces within the vacuum pushing the membrane and structures within and around the vacuum a part; a suction effect produced by electrical charges. This electric charge uses anti-matter and matter, which positively and negatively appose each other within the vacuum. Interestingly Newtonian gravity attracts all solid and isolated particles without any repulsion, or antimatter. But if we follow Newtonian laws of equal and opposite reactions, there must be a repulsion or anti-matter to the attraction used. So why is there no anti-matter? Or is there?

Electromagnetic forces produce waves, which can travel through a vacuum and do not require the presence of a material in order to transport their energy from one location to another. Light waves are an example of electromagnetic waves. Electromagnetic waves are created by the vibration of an electric charge. This vibration creates a wave, which has both an electric and a magnetic component and is random in nature. Due to vibration, sound and light waves being connected, the relationship between these three in the form of photoelectrical effects, warrants further investigation. The energy transport through a medium involves the absorption and reemission of the wave energy and when an electromagnetic wave is absorbed the pace of absorption produces its own wave, which is different from the first and in random configurations due to the expanded energy that is being produced.

Hydrostatic and hydrodynamic pressure can create a

vortex, resulting in positive and negative charges between magnetic and electric forces. Electro hydrodynamics (EHD), which are the dynamics of electrically charged fluids and magneto hydrodynamics (MHD), which are magnetic properties of electrically conducting fluids, both play a part in the biokinesis-ontology body.

Virtual freedom

Virtual freedom or infinity of actions is moving away from the three dimensional ideology and introducing the non-degree of freedom model. Biokinesis-ontology views the human organism and its movement as having open space in which the compliant system can mould itself. This moulding can be universal over the whole of the area and allows the compliant system freedom as it follows no predictable pattern and is asymmetrical. The compliant biokinesis-ontological system moves in the infinity of spiral formations, which are non-symmetrical and omnidirectional throughout and within all layers of biological tissue. It is a complete web with no initial start or end and can travel through any distance (depth and width) that the formation allows.

Thinking back to the classical engineering model with six degrees of freedom and the classical biomechanical model, which uses only three. How does virtual freedom compare? The virtual freedom model is based on floating bones, which are not constrained by the pushing forces of gravity and restricted joint positions but rather contain a joint spaces, which are embedded in the compliant topological structure. These joint spaces contain all the possible positions that the floating bones can move in, in an open space model.

To find the possibility of how many positions or degrees of freedom we have we can combine the six degrees of freedom currently offered. At this stage this is the only maths equation biokinesis-ontology uses, as it indicates how many degrees of freedom are truly available. Let's combine the six degrees of freedom into integrated systems and combine them all together. This can be achieved by using 6x5x4x3x2x1 (6 factorial equation), which equals 720 degrees of freedom available at any bone interaction. If we then use two interactions we get 1440, if three 2160 and so on. So let's take another example:

- 206 bones in the body

- 180 which are movable

- 180 X 720 = 129600 degrees available at any time in a space at any time no matter how big or small and through all movements. This can only occur in a system that follows the ideas of biokinesis-ontology and dynsisation.

So the biokinesis-ontology model has 129600 degrees of freedom available in the internal system where biomechanics has 244.

NB: I still believe that maths is highly problematic when used in the theory of movement. However, I have chosen to include this example here as even if this maths is not 100% correct it shows that using the classical laws with Euclidean shapes in a 3 dimension coordinate systems when describing the human organism is extremely reductionist.

So if in reality there are at least 720 degree of freedom available at virtual joints, then having three dimensional coordinates seems incomplete. With just three degrees of movement available and the range of movement that represents the biological tissues, motion, design and locations seems to narrow down the story of human movement to a model that it far too simplified to be considered accurate. Using a non-Cartesian coordinate system should be used for any biokinesis-ontological and dynisation model systems.

Energy wave Dynamics - moving sounds and vibration: the structure-space model

The structure-space model is the variation in forms of random vibrational sound waves and oscillations produced by the biokinesis-ontology and dynisation models. A sound wave propagates through a structure as a pressure change just like that of fluid, gas or air. Due to the pressure change, there will be an increase in temperature as well as the speed that the wave is travelling at. Therefore, a wave travels faster during the high pressure phase of the oscillation than during the lower pressure phase. This affects the wave's frequency structure and the mobility and stability of the system. This model is characteristic of a non-linear system, since a linear acoustic system responds only to the starting frequency and not to the deflection of frequency found in a non-linear system.

Additionally, waves of different amplitudes will generate different pressure gradients, contributing to the non-linear effect. This nonlinear and random vibration is motion, which is non-deterministic, meaning that future behaviour cannot be precisely predicted. The randomness is a characteristic of the excitation or input reflected throughout the system; this is the true free motion of the wave. This is opposite to the current model used in biomechanics, that an oscillating system is a pattern of motion where all parts of the system move the same, with the same fixed frequency. These fixed frequencies in a system are known as natural frequencies, which are represented by a mechanical object, such as a building, bridge or monument dependant on structure, materials and boundary conditions. This is a mechanical representation of vibration and one which is not representative of true natural frequencies found in living organisms.

In the biokinesis-ontology model the effects of non-linear sound waves leads to the power generated from the vibration itself. The term "energy harvesting" refers to the generation of energy from sources such as vibration along with the hydrodynamic and hydrostat pressure spoken about previously. Converting the available energy from the changes in pressure allows a self-sufficient energy supply to the biokinesis-ontological system. Pressure can be converted via internal and external motion into electrical energy by means of the piezoelectric effect (a structure that can generate an electrical charge), which will transverse non-linear waves and is an oscillation that transfers energy through space of non-rigid objects. Wave motion transfers energy from one point to another, which via the biokinesis-ontological model of a compliant system and virtual freedom models, integrates all biological tissue and especially the interconnections of information from the central nervous system to the brain.

There are two main types of waves found in a biokinesis-ontological system:

1. Non-rigid waves - which propagate through a deformed structure. For example, sound waves propagate via tissue, which integrate with each other, colliding with their neighbours. When air molecules collide, they also bounce away from each other (a restoring force). This keeps the molecules from continuing to travel in the direction of the original wave.

2. Electromagnetic waves - which do not require a medium and is another way an anti-gravity force can be produced. They consist of electrical and magnetic oscillations generated via pressure changes. Electromagnetic waves involve the interaction of repulsion that occurs between electrically charged objects and since all biological tissue is electrical charged, this is of great importance. The electromagnetic force plays a major role in determining the internal properties of all biological tissue, as well as its

motion via the forces of non-uniform and omnidirectional attraction or repulsion.

Electrodynamics and floating bones

Electrodynamic waves are waves that can travel through a vacuum, e.g. sound and vibration. When an electrodynamic wave impinges upon the atoms of a material, the energy of that wave is absorbed. The absorption of energy causes the electrons within the atoms to undergo vibrations. After a short period of vibrational motion, the vibrating electrons create a new electromagnetic wave with the same frequency as the first electromagnetic wave. Once it reaches the next atom, the electromagnetic wave is absorbed, transformed into electron vibrations and then reemitted as an electromagnetic wave.

Bio electrodynamics deals with changing electric and magnetic fields in biological systems, when two objects in each other's vicinity have different electrical charges; i.e. an electrodynamic field exists between them. An electrostatic field also forms around any single object that is electrically charged with respect to its structure. Bio electrodynamics has an attraction and repulsion element to it, as objects attract if their charges are of opposite polarity and objects repel if their charges are of the same polarity. This changes from one polarity to another polarity produces changing bio electrodynamic fields. This can be spoken of as being an electrodynamic wave, which as the ever changing fields move over vast distances through space, make the information universally present throughout the structure.

Vacuum is space void of a structure and is a region where pressure changes occur. When pressure is changed, so does the volume and temperature within the structure. Thermodynamics is a thermal expansion, with the tendency of the structure to change shape, area, and volume in response to a change in temperature or through heat transfer. The temperature dependence of liquid viscosity is such that liquid viscosity tends to decrease (or, alternatively, its fluidity tends to increase) as its temperature increases. This is exactly what synovial fluid achieves as it is a viscous, non-Newtonian fluid found in the vacuums of synovial joints. Due to its property as a non-Newtonian fluid, synovial fluid has a time-dependent increase in viscosity. Or in other words, the longer the fluid undergoes shearing force, the higher its viscosity, the more mobile the fluid. This change of pressure between stability and mobility provides a suction flow within the vacuum created by the electric changes, enabling the bones to float away.

Biotensegrity asserts that due to compression and tension, bones are pulled a part and do not touch due to the tension and compression mechanisms of fascia. However, I propose that what keeps the bones 'floating' and buoyant within the joint space is a result of pressure and electrical changes within the vacuum. In short, the bio electrodynamic changes of attractive and repulsive forces change the electrical charges of the fluid. This in turn change the thermal regulation, and an increased temperature in the synovial fluid produces suction in the vacuum of the joint space. Due to this and increased thermoregulation, the joint space expands and the compliant structure deforms to accommodate for this expansion throughout the body, providing the bone with virtual freedom. This internal hypothesis explaining the 'floating' element of bones within a compliant system replaces the opposing theory of biomechanical levers, providing a way of describing the joints as spaces rather than fixed fulcrums.

Pneudraulics is a word derived from a combination of pneumatics and hydraulics; the science of fluids composed of both liquid and gas and/or air. The concept of fluid power is the use of fluids under pressure to generate, control, and transmit power (energy) thorough out a structure. A fluid power system requires an action like a pump to drive the system. Vibration suits this process, which drives an electro-pneudraulic action where by air and fluid pressure, controlled by an electrical current facilitating a transferral chain from external physical energy due to movement into vibrational internal energy. So the complete chain of the floating bone concept, with relation to a bio-ontological model, consists of the following stages:

1. Stage 1 – physical movement

2. Stage 2 - induces vibration in the bone

3. Stage 3 - electrical impulses released from the bone into the joint space

4. Stage 4 –results in electrical, pneudralic pressure and thermoregulation changes within the joint space

5. Stage 5 – the electrical charge increase, attraction and repulsion occurs

6. Stage 6 - expansion is increased in between the bones and the bones and the joint space become buoyant

Random positioning of higher dimensions or RPOHD: the alternative to the Cartesian coordinate system

Descartes believed all physical objects must be explained in terms of maths and everything could be equated and documented as such. He devised the Cartesian coordinate system based on lines to represent objects in space.

Biological structures, cannot realistically be represented in the geometry of space by three straight lines, as it is in the coordinate system. There must be further development and a more realistic model for understanding the biological structure in space. One such view, which is compatible with the bio-ontological perspective is that of random positioning, with hidden dimensions. Random positioning of higher dimensions or RPOHD acts like a crumpled ball of paper; a topological shape change. With infinite curves and surfaces, which are never repeated twice, asymmetrical and with different variations in depth, size, shape and thickness of the formations.

This suggest that even though from an external Cartesian coordinate model, straight lines can be drawn to form a box for any shape and provide three dimensions the truth is that due to the infinite variations found within this RPOHD many more hidden dimensions can be found. Therefore, it is not possible to find a single number to justify the whole, as there are so many more hidden dimensions that the three conventional dimensions being spoken about. These internally hidden dimensions are hidden between the layers of the RPOHD structure that interchange amongst themselves, quickly and randomly. The greater the deformation that is occurring the more non uniform it becomes. The problem is that to quantify any RPOHD numbers in accordance with current mechanical laws and mathematics is not possible.

Summary

It is important to remember that the components of the biokinesis-ontological theory of the new biomechanics act on their own behalf, towards their own ends. Fundamentally, the design is internal, arising from within, and serving no other purpose than to maintain its own organization. A biomechanical machine is also organized, of course, given that the operation of each part is dependent on it being properly arranged with respect to every other part and to the system as a whole. But in an organism, the parts are not just there for the sake of each other but they also produce each other, repair each other, and generally exist by means of one another. This approach founded in holism is the foundation of biokinesis-ontology theory.

The cutting edge hypothesis of biokinesis-ontology seeks to change the way we understand human movement. For simplicity this new road map of human movement theory can be broken down into three sections:

1. Prerequisite principles.

Biokinesis-ontology recognises certain prerequisite principles in the body:

a.   Holism

b.   Complex systems

c.   Systems theory and systems biology

d.   Non-linear systems

e.   Synergistics

f.   Emergence

g.   Self-organisation

h.   Sub-optimisation

i.   Non-mathematical topology

    j.   Vitalism

    k.   Holonomic systems

    l.   Morphological elasticity.

2. Recognised states

Biokinesis-ontology recognises certain states within the body, including:

    a.   A non-lever system.

    b.   An integrally compliant system.

    c.   The internal body as a non-gravity system.

    d.   Adheres to dynisation; the process of dynamic and complex organisation.

    e.   A presegrity structure; a hydrodynamic and hydrostatic system, working as a pressurized integral system.

    f.   Semi-solid. Semi-elastic system.

3. Proposed properties

Biokinesis-ontology proposes certain reactions, capabilities and properties of the body, based upon the prerequisite principles and recognised states:

a. An integral, complete system that operates as a whole.

b. Stiff enough to bear loads, yet supple enough to transfer force and vibration.

c. Consisting of joint spaces rather than conventional joints.

d. Joint spaces create the concept of 'floating bones' via the pneudraulic and bio electromagnetic systems.

e. Without internal friction.

f. Able to absorb and pass on vibrational forces.

g. Capable of virtual freedom.

Conclusion

"New questions can produce new scientific leaps. They can tiddlywink new flips of insight and understanding. Big ones. Paradigm shifts".

- Howard Bloom

The preceding chapters have looked at how biomechanics has evolved; outlined the problems we encounter by associating living, moving human beings with the mechanistic, biomechanical view; and hinted towards the future of how we might think about, analyse and understand the theory of human movement from a more complete, logical and multifaceted perspective.

The information in the future section of this book has never been spoken about or presented before in this context; to my knowledge this is the first book of its kind to look at the theory of human movement from a completely new angle, without the constraints of outdated machine ideology at the core. This work is based purely on my own views, which I have evolved and pieced together over many years from my scientific education, practical understanding and physical experience of how the body really moves. And in truth, that is my main aim; to evolve the theory of human movement to a level where it accurately reflects reality so the way we understand, describe and experience what is happening in the body is in alignment, allowing us to connect with the physicality of the body rather than the theory of movement being an abstract, mathematical pattern. How we speak about and analyse movement should be how we move; it should reflect reality.

I am expecting this book to be considered highly controversial due to the novelty of the ideas expressed. From purely academic movement theorists I am predicting a backlash. Bring it on! I am ready for the debate. But putting the pure theorists aside for a minute; this book is designed for people who understand human movement from the inside out and I am hopeful that for people who understand movement intrinsically, with their own bodies that they will understand that the current theoretical roadmap we have of human movement is not serving our best interests.

Hopefully, you have enjoyed the trip down the rabbit hole. This book is just the beginning. I am positive that the more awareness is brought to this subject, the more it will adapt, evolve and grow. However, before any of that can occur there needs to be a start. And this book is the start of the evolution of biomechanics. I intend to follow this introduction to the topic of movement theory with my next book Biokinesis-ontology for a more in-depth look at the future of movement theory. So watch this space...

Does the mechanistic, deterministic, man as a machine based theory suffice or is it time to move towards movement theory that expands to define our bodies as a biokinesis-ontological, integrally compliant, pressurised and self-organising system?

I always love to connect with people about movement, so please feel free to join the movement theory revolution, get in touch and share your views...

Yours in movement

Stephen Braybrook

The Movement Man

www.themovementman.com
https://www.facebook.com/movementman
https://www.facebook.com/brainmoveeducation/
Twitter - @BraybrookSJ

8013277R00137

Printed in Germany
by Amazon Distribution
GmbH, Leipzig